IT'S MY LIFE, TOO!

THRIVE AND STAY ALIVE AS A
CAREGIVER

DAVE NASSANEY

Published by
Hybrid Global Publishing
301 E 57th Street, 4th fl
New York, NY 10022

Manufactured in the United States of America, or in the United Kingdom when distributed elsewhere.

Nassaney, Dave
    It's my Life, Too! Thrive and Stay Alive as a Caregiver
LCCN: 2017951465
Paperback: 978-1-938015-77-9
eBook: 978-1-938015-78-6

Interior design: Claudia Volkman
Editing by: Claudia Volkman
Photo credits: Dave Nassaney

A big thank you goes out, first to God for His miraculous provision in providing me with a great wife and a relatively "low-maintenance" care-receiver, and second, to that same care-receiver and wife of mine, Charlene, who constantly reminds me that it doesn't matter how bad your circumstances are, if my wife can live above hers with a smile on her face, and faith in her heart, so can I . . . and so can YOU!

TABLE OF CONTENTS

FOREWORD

PEOPLE IN BUSINESS always like to ask in their training seminars, "What is your why?" After all, one's "'why" is one's story. It's one's passion. I think a proper introduction of myself should start with me sharing *my* "why." I'll be brief here and give more details later in this book.

My "why" is simply my wife, and what happened to us in September of 1996. We had a fairy-tale courtship, romance and marriage for the first twenty-one years of our lives together. We were sitting together on the couch one morning, having a conversation, when my wife complained to me of a bad headache that she had had for a few days. We didn't pay much attention to it; I mean, it was only a headache. If she went to the doctor, he would probably just tell her, "Take two aspirin and call me in the morning." Well, like I said, we didn't worry–

that is until is ceased being *only* a headache. Then, things quickly went from bad to worse. By the time the ambulance arrived, it was too late. Charlene had a massive stroke, and our world immediately turned upside-down and has never been the same.

Our kids were already grown, and only our eighteen-year-old still lived in our home. It wouldn't be long before we entered the "empty-nest" phase of life that we had always looked forward to. But instead, I found myself having to constantly care for the "love of my life" 24/7. There is no way that anyone can ever prepare for that. To be honest, the first two years were a living hell for us. I didn't know what I was doing. I didn't know how to care for my wife, and I didn't know who Charlene was anymore.

In time, she became angry and bitter because she was grieving her loss, and then I became angry and bitter because I was grieving my loss. I grieved that my wife was no longer the woman that I married. I still loved her, but it was so hard being on the receiving end of all that anger brought about by her grief.

I felt so guilty. In fact, I came to a point one day that I didn't know if I could do it any longer. I sat down and wrote her a letter. I told her, "Charlene, why are you so mean to me? It's so hard being your husband taking care of you all the time. I know it's hard for you, but you are making it even harder for me to care for you. I just don't know if I can be with you any longer. I'll take care of you financially, but I just can't be with you."

I wrote that letter, and I read that letter over and over again, but I just couldn't give it to her. It is truly how I felt in that moment. But I wanted to love my wife. I wanted to care for her. I wanted to have a loving relationship with the woman that I had married so many years ago, but it seemed impossible because she was so angry most of the time, and she usually pointed that anger at me, the only one around. I just didn't know if there was any hope for us anymore. I didn't know how to care for my wife. I didn't know if I even wanted to.

So, rather than divorce her or separate or do any of those things, I just had to get out of the house. I left her mother in charge, and I hopped on a plane to visit some friends and relatives out of state for the weekend. I had to think and get some perspective. Being a positive person all my life, I was not used to experiencing these negative feelings.

When I returned, I felt extremely rested and recharged. It felt so good. I had a much better outlook and attitude on life. I even remembered that someone at the hospital invited me to a caregiver's support group for people just like me, burned-out caregivers. Going to that group changed everything for me. I found hope again, and I discovered that I had to take care of me before I could take care of my wife.

They tell us on airplanes that, in the event of an emergency, we are to put our oxygen mask on first, before we attempt to help our loved ones with their mask. That's such a great metaphor for all of life. You have to take care of yourself first, not out of selfishness, but out of survival. If I couldn't take care of me, how could I possibly take care of Charlene?

When I finally realized how much I was able to change, to my surprise, my wife also changed. I was no longer thinking about how she made me feel. I was just taking care of me, so I could take care of her. Then I realized that there are so many caregivers out there taking care of a spouse, a child, a parent, a sister, a brother, or a loved one who had a tragic, unexpected incident in their lives. They are going through this pain, and I want to help them triumph over that pain. I don't want them to give up like I almost gave up. I don't want their relationships to suffer anymore.

After two years, when Charlene finally reached the "acceptance" stage of her grief, she became her old self again. I am very proud of her. She was, and still is, a cross between Martha Stewart and Wonder

Woman. She is truly amazing. She is like a one-armed wallpaper hanger. She makes us "normal" people really look like whiners and complainers. She is my hero.

INTRODUCTION

IT'S MY LIFE, TOO!, based on my popular radio show, *Dave, The Caregiver's Caregiver,* is a practical self-help book that empowers those new to long-term caregiving to provide top-quality care to their loved ones while avoiding burnout and having satisfying, fulfilling lives of their own.

Long-term caregivers desperately need this information because burnout is currently at epidemic proportions. One third of the U.S. population is currently caring for a loved one without receiving any compensation and have put their lives and careers on hold for an undetermined period of time. They often feel like they are in caregiver prison and become isolated, hopeless, and depressed. As the baby boomers continue to age, these numbers will only increase. It has been said that there are three types of people in the world; those who will become caregivers, those who are caregivers, and those who will need a caregiver.

Reputable studies have indicated that caregiver stress and burnout can shorten a caregiver's life by as much as four to eight years. While the primary focus of care usually concentrates on the person who has suffered an accident, illness, or condition that renders them dependent on the care of others, we are realizing that the primary caregiver, often a spouse, child, or parent, usually shoulders the responsibility and is also in need of assistance.

It's My Life, Too! provides encouragement and easy-to-implement steps to prevent caregiver burnout. Caregivers who are already exhibiting symptoms of burnout will also be able to apply these same techniques and insights to immediately decrease stress and the significant health dangers to their own well-being. When a crisis occurs and a loved one has an accident or medical emergency, the caregiver is plunged into a complex redefinition of their role that affects their self-image of who they had to become to survive this new and unexpected occupation.

There is no book on the market that addresses the needs of long-term caregivers regardless of the challenges faced by their loved ones. Most books focus on specific illnesses or conditions such as survivors of stroke, head or spinal injuries, dementia and Alzheimer's, or parenting a disabled child. Additionally, books tend to lump all caregivers into one group–those dealing with short-term illnesses, those facing end-of-life issues, and long-term care. Caring for someone who is expected to live for a relatively long period of time with an illness or condition poses specific and unique challenges for the caregiver. This book pinpoints the needs and strategies of this population. While some books focus on "surviving" long-term caregiving, *It's My Life, Too!* demonstrates that the life of the caregiver is of equal importance and shows that caregiving can be a rewarding and gratifying experience.

It's My Life, Too! assists the caregiver in consciously and intentionally making seven key decisions that all long-term caregivers face, thereby empowering them to avoid feelings of victimization or resentment. Using examples from my life as a caregiver as well as those with whom I work, my goal is to provide the reader with an awareness that others are successfully navigating these difficult challenges which allow them to say "Yes" to their own happiness and well-being. The book is intentionally designed for adequate white space so as not to overwhelm the reader with large blocks of text. The sentence structure and vocabulary is aimed at sixth grade, with an effort to avoid technical language or insider jargon.

TAKEAWAYS

- Often caregivers unnecessarily sacrifice their own lives to provide long-term care for their loved ones. Readers are encouraged to focus attention on their own needs, and create a long-term plan so that they, as well as their loved ones, experience life to its fullest.

- Readers are given practical techniques that can be immediately applied to their lives to decrease stress and increase a sense of well-being, health, and optimism.

- Exercises are provided that help caregivers assess their ability to care for themselves, monitor their stress level and vulnerability to burnout, and employ specific strategies to have their needs addressed while insuring that their loved ones receive quality care.

- Readers are reminded that they are not alone; millions of people are caregivers and many online and local resources are available to them.

- Readers are encouraged to claim the right to their own life, rather than allow their lives to be defined by caregiving alone.

- The book provides steps caregivers can take to create a support team network, including those in the medical field, siblings, relatives, friends and volunteers.

- Readers will receive an understanding of the difference between the natural process of grief, and falling into a clinical depression.

CHAPTER 1

THE TWO MOST IMPORTANT WORDS YOU'LL USE AS A CAREGIVER

ARE YOU A caregiver? Welcome to the club. We all have our story of how we got here and how we are doing so far. Some of you are not doing very well. Some of you are at your wits end. And some of you are ready to throw in the towel. You'll want to keep reading. I believe I can help. Let me begin by sharing some background of how I got here.

It was early on a Sunday morning in 1996. I awoke from a deep sleep to find that my wife, Charlene, was not in our bed. The clock showed 6:28 a.m. It was unlike Charlene to be up so early. I called out her name, but she did not respond. *Perhaps she's in the bathroom,* I thought to myself. *Is she not feeling well? Did her three-day headache return?*

I called out to her again, still with no response. I searched the house and heard the television in the family room, with what sounded like an old Shirley Temple movie. This didn't make sense. She wasn't a television watcher. And if she did see a show now and then, she was definitely not an early riser. Something was terribly wrong.

I followed the sounds of the TV and found her on the couch. She didn't look up. I asked if she was OK, and she mumbled that her headache was throbbing and that the pain circled her head like a crown. I asked if she would like me to massage her forehead as I had done a day earlier to give her some relief. She answered yes.

I knelt in front of her and slowly massaged above her eyes. I saw her face, yet I could not adjust my mind to what was in front of me. It took me a moment or two to recognize that her face, the precious face of the person I have loved for so many years, was distorted. Her body slumped. I asked her to say something—anything. This time her mouth moved, but no words and no sounds reached my ears, as if a mute button had been pushed.

I was not well informed about strokes back on that fateful Sunday morning in 1996, but I somehow knew she was having a stroke and that I needed to dial 9-1-1 as fast as my body could make it to the phone. To my relief, the paramedics arrived quickly, and they confirmed to me that Charlene was indeed suffering from a stroke. The tantamount concern was for Charlene's life itself, which required getting her to the hospital as quickly as possible. The paramedics knew exactly how to handle her medical crisis. Their competence helped me cope with the emotional and mental chaos that overtook me at that moment.

Unfortunately, it wasn't until later on that I realized my confidence was poorly placed. There is only a three-hour window to address the symptoms of a stroke before brain damage occurs. The paramedics recommended we go to the closer and smaller hospital to get her help more quickly. Unfortunately, the facility was not as well-equipped to handle her stroke as the larger medical center just ten minutes farther down the road—to which she was eventually transferred. Due to that decision which delayed her proper care, I absolutely believe that Charlene lost her speech and became permanently paralyzed on her right side. Life is a series of decisions, and I shall regret this one as long as we both shall live.

I didn't understand at the time the full extent of what was happening, but from that morning on, our lives have never been the same. Charlene suffered a permanent disability, and I instantly became her caregiver. I had no idea how to take care of the woman I loved in this way, a woman who had been vibrant, competent, and very independent. It was extremely difficult for both of us, in different ways, to create a new way of living and relating to one another.

I do not know what event catapulted you into your current role as caregiver, but most likely someone you love suffered an accident, illness, or other life-altering experience. The good news is that they survived. The stressful reality is that now they rely on you more than ever. Perhaps you're a parent of a child who was born handicapped or has become disabled and now requires more attention than expected. Or your partner or spouse may be facing permanent or long-term limitations, no longer able to care for themselves as in the past. As the baby boomer generation ages, more adult children are caring for their aging parents while at the same time still raising their own families.

Regardless of the specifics that have put you in this place, you and I have something very significant in common. We both love people who need us, and we are committed to caring for them. This book will teach you that the well-being of the care-receiver depends on your well-being. To be competent caregivers, *we must find a new way to live our own lives* while we take care of someone we dearly love.

If you ever sat by a loved one's bed and wondered how you would be able to handle this new, overwhelming responsibility, then you're reading the right book. It can feel like you're all alone, and there's no one out there to help or support you. But the fact is that you're not alone. I want you to know that I've sat where you're sitting right now. I've felt the feelings that are pressing down on you. And I've got a very important message—you can *more than* survive this situation. You can actually live out your new role with confidence.

Your life has been radically changed. I won't minimize it, but your life has not come to an end either. You can still have a wonderful, satisfying future in spite of, or even because of, your loved one's dependency on you. I know this to be true because it happened to me. I've learned how to deal with tragedy and difficulty and have not merely "survived"—I am living a wonderful life.

I'm going to show you how to avoid the common mistakes many long-term caregivers make that set them up for needless stress and burnout. You'll learn how to take great care of yourself while providing top quality care for your loved one. I will explain how I became a long-term caregiver. You

IT'S MY LIFE, TOO!

may have thought that you had nothing in common with anyone. Not true. Honestly, I suspect you'll find that you and I have a great deal in common.

Two Important Words

The two most important words you'll use as a caregiver are "Yes" and "No."

You might be very good at saying "Yes," or maybe you didn't have the choice to say "No." A lot of people, especially caregivers, want to help others. Either way, it's also common for caregivers to take on much more than they can handle, and this can lead to some negative results:

- Feeling guilty for letting other people down

- Resentful about having too much to do for others

- Feeling obligated to sacrifice their own needs

When our loved ones were in the throes of their trauma, focusing on their needs was the appropriate response. I was by Charlene's side when she was in the hospital, and fighting for her life. I suspect when illness struck or the accident occurred or the tragedy hit, you put your life on hold and did everything you could to help your loved one. Nights in the hospital. Days off work. Questions asked. Records kept. You gave your total attention to the crisis as adrenaline pulsed through your veins and your mind tried to remain singularly focused.

It's common for caregivers to live on adrenaline, late night cups of coffee and heightened emotions day after day after day. In fact, it can become a lifestyle if we're not careful. When I was basically living at the hospital for a week or two, I didn't realize that I hadn't been home to change clothes, shower, eat or even sleep until a family member brought it to my attention. It was very easy and natural for me to just stay there by Charlene's side, visit with the friends and family who stopped by her room, snack on the food trays they would bring her that she didn't eat, and take cat naps with her in her bed while the night nurse looked the other way. I was depriving myself of rest, nourishment, exercise and personal hygiene.

When my daughter finally *forced* me to go home, I fell into my bed and slept for fifteen hours. When I got up, I took a hot bath and ate some wonderful leftovers that my wife had frozen. It felt so good to have my needs met again. I finally realized that I was killing myself with neglect. My wife never even missed me while I was recovering that day, and no one made me feel guilty for taking a break. It was an eye-opener for me that life goes on, and I *must* put my needs first. Sure, it was hard in the beginning, but when I saw the consequences of neglecting my health, and I realized that I would *never* let my loved ones do that, I made it my policy from that point on that I would go home every night from the hospital. That policy continues at home today, taking frequent breaks from my duties as a caregiver.

Strong emotions such as fear and anger are meant for short-term situations. But they will destroy us, physically, emotionally, and spiritually, if we say "Yes" to them on a long-term basis. I remember a time when I first realized that my beautiful, articulate wife might never be able to speak in sentences again. Discovering that we could no longer have deep conversations, walks on the beach, or walk *anywhere*, I was afraid, and I was angry. But it didn't take more than two days before I felt this pain in my stomach. I felt like I was giving myself an ulcer. Can you imagine if I allowed myself to go on for months or years carrying around that fear and anger? Many caregivers often suffer from colitis and stomach bleeds. I am so glad that I quickly learned the benefits of saying "No" to such strong emotions as fear and anger.

You may not be as dependent upon others to

meet your needs, but your needs are as valid as those of your loved one. It is equally important to have your needs met as it is for the person who is in need of special care. Making priorities, balancing your commitments, assessing and deciding the best course of action for your care-receiver, and learning new skills will all make you a better caregiver. Just because you can walk better than a two-year-old doesn't mean that you can walk a tightrope without practice. Anytime you're trying a new thing...it will feel unfamiliar to you, even uncomfortable or painful at first.

I am an entrepreneur. I run a business. I hire and fire people. I balance books, buy and sell inventory and pay the bills. I didn't think I had what it took to be a caregiver back then. I was really good at making money and balancing budgets. But to take care of my wife's stroke symptoms of speech impairment and paralysis, be her voice, her legs, her hands? Not me. I didn't believe I could do it at the time. I was scared. I was angry at myself for not demanding that the paramedics take her to the big medical center, instead of the closer, smaller "rinky-dink" private hospital. That decision caused her to not get the proper medications that would have dissolved her blood clot and prevented brain damage. But what choice did I have at the time? I didn't know anything about strokes. I had to forgive myself and move on with what happened. I took it one day at a time. The days rolled into weeks, the weeks into months, months into years, and eventually into a couple of decades. I ultimately learned what to do and how to do it by trial and error. Fortunately for me (and my wife), it was sooner rather than later. Now you can benefit from all my mistakes.

For example, I have never really dressed a woman before–you know, underwear, bras, support stockings, and those shoes and buttons! Oh, how I hate those shoes! They never go on easily, just like Cinderella's stepsister's foot that wouldn't fit into the glass slipper. And those buttons, all sizes and shapes! The smaller the button, the more impossible it is to button it through that tiny button hole. I know it sounds silly, but I believe that's why God made zippers and slippers that have no buckles . . . just for caregivers.

Batteries and Boundaries

If you are miserable, you won't be able to provide hope and comfort to your loved one. If you feel exhausted, like a dying battery, you will be unable to accurately recognize their needs or properly care for them. With the best of intentions, you may undermine your health and well-being and become ill yourself.

There are times when you must acknowledge that your life is important and say "No."

Saying "No" can be hard because most of us have been taught to feel guilty about it. We feel selfish. If you've been brought up in a Christian home, you have probably been taught that to sacrifice yourself for others is a spiritual virtue. Jesus sacrificed Himself for us, so we are to sacrifice ourselves for others, right?

I believe that we are to follow Christ's example and serve each other. As caregivers, service is the primary thing we do every day. But there is nothing noble about burning yourself out. Jesus often went away from the crowds to replenish Himself. He would habitually go away by Himself into the mountains to meditate and pray to His heavenly Father. He was under so much stress while speaking to the large crowds. He had to debate the religious leaders, avoid His enemies from stoning Him, raise the dead, heal the sick, walk on water during a severe storm at sea, take frequent naps in the back of the boat, feed the multitudes with only five fish and two loaves of bread, be the peacekeeper to His disciple's frequent arguments amongst each other, keep them safe, and so on. He definitely knew how to squeeze in His "me" time. Remember, the Bible says that He was 100 percent man and 100 percent God, so His body was subject to the same limitations as ours (hunger, thirst, pain, temptations, stress, etc.).

He also maintained important relationships with His friends who supported and cared for Him. That's right; Jesus had a support group . . . actually many. His heavenly Father was His best support. He could tell Him anything (good venting time). His disciples were a support for Him as well, helping Him do the hard work of His ministry. His mother was a huge emotional support, especially during His last days on earth. He had other close friends like Mary, Martha, and their brother, Lazarus, whom Jesus wept over when he died and then raised from the dead because He loved him so much.

The concept of believing that I was not alone, that God was there with me, was invaluable. I remember feeling like that famous picture of the two footprints in the sand, where there were only one set of footprints during the most difficult of times. That was because God was carrying me (as well as my wife) in His arms. I felt like I was floating on air, as though my feet never touched the ground during those really tough couple of years in the beginning of her stroke.

For example, I remember in the hospital being visited by dozens and dozens of loving people offering their support and prayers for what happened.

Singers we know came into the hospital room to sing to my wife and I beautiful uplifting songs that were such a blessing. Weeks and weeks went by that God would inspire certain people to help us and offer their prayers of encouragement each and every day. It just felt so good, and I remember thanking God for sending these wonderful people to comfort us. It was like I was floating on air, and the nasty circumstances below us were not even close enough to touch us.

While we strive to become more like Christ, we must not start to believe that we are limitless and all-powerful like God is. It's easy to forget that we are limited human beings who deserve to live rich, fulfilling, and even fun lives.

Saying "No" sets a boundary that protects you from excessive stress and self-destruction. A lot of people who need you to take care of them do not like to be told "No." This may be especially true of your dependent loved one. But there are times to say "No," and this book equips you to know when and shows you how to say "No."

Don't misunderstand me—I'm not saying that you should abandon your loved one or leave them uncared for. Not at all. I want to show you how to say "Yes" to both yourself and to the person you love in such a way that you can be the caregiver you want to be.

Let's Talk About You

At the end of each chapter, I will invite you to focus solely on yourself. You can write your responses in this book, or use a journal to record your thoughts, feelings, and decisions. You spend a great deal of your time and energy attending to the needs of others. This will be a time just for you. You deserve and need time to reflect on yourself. I know this is so because I am a caregiver myself. Let's talk about you.

- Did you have the luxury of planning ahead? Or were you surprised by a tragedy? Preparing for the expected changes will equip you to better to deal with this change in your life. What do you expect will happen in the next days, weeks, months?

- How are you handling this "New Normal?"

- Do you ever feel resentment towards your care-receiver? If so, why?

- Do you ever feel like giving up?

- What is your greatest joy of caregiving?

CHAPTER 2

SAY "YES" TO CAREGIVING;
SAY "NO" TO BURNOUT

YOU MIGHT FEEL as if you have no choice in your new role as caregiver. Your loved one needs your help and that's all there is to it. You're stuck. But the fact is, you actually *do* have a choice. There are people who turn away from this kind of responsibility, and abandon their friends or family members in various ways. Some parents leave their children in the care of others when the going gets difficult. I know of children with disabilities ending up in foster care or in institutions because their parents did not fulfill their responsibility to their children. Many marriages have broken up over the weight of caregiving. And adult children of aging parents are known to ignore their duty, perhaps putting the entire responsibility on a sibling or other family member. Some people act "as if" they are stepping up to the plate, while in reality they go through the motions without any warmth or nurturance.

For example, I have a gas station, and I remember a time when a particular adult child who was caring for his very old father came into the store to pay for his fuel. Without the son realizing it, his elderly dad followed him inside instead of staying in the car as he was told. When he turned around and saw his dad, he yelled at him, "What are you doing here? I told you to stay in the car. You always do this. Why don't you ever listen to me?" The disrespect that this man showed his father in a public place is inexcusable. Just imagine what else goes on at home. This caregiver may think he is doing a noble job stepping up to the plate (and he is), but in reality he is just going through the motions.

I observed others who have not dealt very well with such life-changing experiences. Some seem destined to live a life full of constant hopelessness, depression and despair. Others constantly fight with each other until their marriage can no longer survive the strife, and then divorce puts the final nail in their marriage coffin. Still others decide to end their lives with a gun or an overdose of pills. I share my story with you so that you can avoid making a difficult situation become even worse. We all know about these types of situations where someone says "No" to caring for a family member or friend. Promises are broken and commitments are left unfilled because people aren't willing to stay and care. I stopped counting the number of care-receivers who told me that their caregiver/spouse filed divorce papers against them while still in the hospital or shortly afterward. The bottom line is that life doesn't stop giving us problems just because we became a caregiver or a care-receiver. But I like to think that God gives us caregivers an extra special portion of His grace to help us cope with all that "stuff" that life throws our way.

Say "Yes" to Caregiving

But you and I do take our responsibilities seriously. We made a commitment to someone and now, through the difficult times, we intend to fulfill that commitment. I think it's extremely important for those of us who are long-term caregivers to acknowledge that we have made a courageous and loving choice. Not everyone says "Yes," and it's a decision that you can be proud of.

I have found in my own situation, and with the thousands of people who listen and respond to my radio show, *Dave, The Caregiver's Caregiver,* that it's critical we caregivers make an intentional decision to become our loved one's caregiver. When you make that choice, you discard the role of victim. You remind yourself that you have options and have chosen a specific path. It's an empowering decision to make, and if you ever feel resentful or discouraged in the future, you can look back on the day when you chose to become a caregiver.

It is true that you may not have had the chance to intentionally decide to become a caregiver, like me. One second I was a normal person, and the next second I was my wife's caregiver. It happened that quickly. I didn't even know what a caregiver was. Someone had to tell me that I was one. I feel that I was one of the lucky ones, however, because I loved my wife so much that I was always there for her. This new and different experience was just an extension of that love. The real test is after you have been doing this caregiving thing for many years or decades and still have the love, respect, compassion and dedication for your loved one that you did when you first started.

Say "No" to Burnout

When you and I said "Yes" to becoming caregivers, we did not say "And therefore, I can have no life."

Our lives are just as important as our loved ones. When we say "Yes" to caring for them, we must also say "Yes" to caring for ourselves. It's tempting for us to put their needs and lives at a higher place of importance than we do our own.

It is extremely important to say "No" to burnout. Today you are the same person, with the same God-given purpose, as you were prior to your loved one's accident or illness. You have a separate identity, a specific calling and a responsibility to your own life. Living your life well is just as important as it is for your loved one. It's not simply a right—it's a responsibility for you to take excellent care of yourself.

You may feel so overwhelmed at the moment that all you can do is put one foot in front of the other. That's completely understandable and acceptable. Make the commitment to be a caregiver one day at a time, if needed. Say "Yes" to yourself and to your loved one.

A lot of caregivers I speak with act as if burnout is something that is inevitable, out of their control, and something that happens to them. In reality, caregiver burnout is the result of a series of self-destructive choices a caregiver makes to ignore their own needs. Caregiver burnout doesn't happen overnight. You must work at burning yourself out over an extended period of time.

You need to realize that the different problems we caregivers experience in life over the years are likely the result of a series of bad decisions we made during those same years. Decisions might include stopping your gym membership, allowing your friendships to die on the vine, skipping meals, snapping at people you would usually not snap at, not scheduling enough sleep for your body to function, not asking for help, allowing your performance at work to be compromised so that it could result in you being fired, not taking breaks from your loved one, and not nurturing the relationship you have with your care-receiver.

It is possible, however, to reverse most problems relating to years of bad decision-making by consciously deciding to make a series of good decisions that will also likely take years. If we just commit to one good decision a day, or a week, we can eventually escape the terrible symptoms of burnout. Examples would be the opposite of the ones I listed above, such as keeping that gym membership, asking for help, and taking breaks, etc.

Burnout takes many forms. Here are just a few:

Physical Exhaustion

Are you tired most of the time, but have a hard time sleeping? Do you wake up with a sense of dread at the idea of getting through another difficult day? It's common for burned-out caregivers to lose their appetites or overeat to compensate for the increased demands they face.

Does your body feel "different" than it used to feel? Some who are in a stage of burnout experience chest pains, dizziness, stomach and digestive problems, headaches, back aches, and other painful conditions. It's common for caregivers to become sick, unable to fight off flus, colds and other viral and bacterial infections with a compromised immune system. How can you adequately care for your loved one if you're sick in bed yourself?

Begin your burnout-free journey by thinking healthy. Healthy thinking has to start with a healthy attitude. A healthy attitude is a positive attitude, a hopeful attitude, and a possibility attitude. If we don't have a positive image for our life, then our life will become a self-fulfilling prophecy of that negative image. Our subconscious has no idea if something is attainable unless you tell it so. It doesn't know any better; it can't discern if something is impossible or not. It listens to your beliefs. If you confess it to yourself and others, and believe it is possible, your subconscious will believe you and do everything to make it happen.

So many caregivers I meet have a hopeless and

fatalistic attitude about their future. Now I know that many of you have it really, really bad, and I feel your pain; I really do. But no matter how bad it is, having a positive attitude, some faith, and a clear head can help you solve almost any impossible situation. Try it—it really works, and if it doesn't, then find a close friend who is not "stuck in your "subconscious" to help you see where you are having difficulty acquiring a positive attitude. It is a matter of life, and a slow, painful death.

Emotional Exhaustion

Three of the most common emotional symptoms of burnout are excessive anxiety, clinical depression, and irritability that quickly erupts into anger. Now, let's be realistic. You are facing an enormous change in your life—one that you did not choose. So feeling anxious, sad, and angry are normal and acceptable emotions. The problem is not the kind of feeling you have, but the depth and length of time these emotions grip you.

Grieving the loss of what your life used to be is critical for you to survive and even thrive. Everyone who suffers loss must grieve whether they want to or not. It is a normal, healthy process. Don't stay in denial about your loss, but instead allow yourself to grieve. It is OK to cry and to feel sad about what happened, but getting stuck is not a healthy grief. You need to move through the stages of grief until you reach the acceptance of your loss. You may still be sad, but you will be on your way to true healing.

For those of you who have never heard, the five stages of grief according to Elizabeth Keebler are as follows: Denial, Anger, Bargaining, Depression, and Acceptance. In this chapter, I merely want to describe what burnout may look like in your life, to assess whether you are taking proper care of yourself or heading for difficulty.

Overwhelm

If you no longer participate in the activities you used to love, or spending time with those who nurture and support you, then burnout is soon to follow. It's natural to want to avoid pain. But if we detach because we are overwhelmed, we are robbed of the enjoyment of life.

The world seems dreary. All we notice are the disappointments and the sadness. We may be drawn to watching negative news stories or sharing negative comments on social media. Burnout shows itself with a lack of proper care for our loved one, a sense of hopelessness and asking ourselves, "Why me?"

You May Feel Alone, but You're Not Alone

It was amazing for me to learn that 65.7 million caregivers make up 29 percent of the U.S. adult population providing care to someone who is ill, disabled or aged (U.S. National Alliance for Caregiving; Washington, DC; updated November 2012.) Look at these stats:

- 43.5 million adult family caregivers care for someone over fifty years of age and 14.9 million care for someone who has Alzheimer's disease or other dementia.

- Caregiver services were valued at $450 billion per year in 2009- up from $375 billion in year 2007. The value of unpaid family caregivers will likely continue to be the largest source of long-term care services in the U.S.

- The aging population, sixty-five and older, will more than double between the years 2000 and 2030, increasing to 71.5 million from 35.1 million in 2000.

These are alarming statistics given the huge potential for caregiver burnout now and in the foreseeable future. We do not know how many caregivers are in the process of burning out, but I'm glad you are reading this book. I don't want you to become a statistic by becoming a burned out caregiver.

Not burning out requires a choice. And burning out requires a choice as well. Burned out caregivers choose to ignore their own needs. It's not something that happens "to you" but only occurs when *you* allow it.

Burnout is avoidable, but it takes an intentional commitment on your part. The good thing is—you are great at making commitments, right? You're "hanging in there" with your loved one through thick and thin. You're also a great caregiver. All you need to do is focus your amazing talent at recognizing someone's need by looking at yourself, not someone else.

If you burn out, you will suffer. Your loved one will suffer. And the fact is, you could become ill and your life span reduced. A six-year study conducted by Dr. Janice Kiecolt-Glaser found that spouses of Alzheimer's patients had a 63 percent higher death rate than those of the same age who were not caregivers. We all know that stress-related diseases are on the rise.

We have all boarded an airplane to fly somewhere only to have the flight attendants direct our attention to the video explaining their emergency procedures. They usually go on to say,

"In the unlikely event of a loss in cabin pressure, your oxygen masks will fall from the compartment above your seat. Reach up and pull down on the mask until the tubing is fully extended. Place the mask over your nose and mouth, secure it with the elastic band and breathe normally. The oxygen bag may not appear to inflate, however, oxygen is flowing. *For those of you traveling with small children, adjust your mask* first *and* **then** *assist the child.*"

Isn't that the most selfish thing you have ever heard? Can you imagine telling a parent to put *their* mask on *first*, when their little bundle of joy is sitting right next to them gasping for air? I wonder how many parents actually follow directions in an emergency and put their mask on first? I suspect that many have disobeyed the flight attendant. I know they have been told again and again that same message every time they board a flight. How could passengers possibly obey the flight attendant's unreasonable and selfish instructions against a little child? We would gladly throw ourselves in front of a speeding locomotive for that little one.

In fact, I don't even know if *I* could be trusted to follow directions about the oxygen mask if my frightened little girl was screaming at me to help her with her mask before I was able to put on mine. How can you know what you would do in a real emergency as your plane is diving down into the ocean, and screams surround you in the cabin while the engine is in flames? What is the purpose of that silly rule anyway?

I can safely assume that before they made this instruction on airlines, they discovered that passengers were blacking out in the process of helping their kids and other needy passengers with their masks. Obviously, if you black out, you cannot help anyone, especially yourself. This is a great analogy that paints a vivid picture of the way we caregivers do not prioritize our self-care, which can be deadly for us.

I am committed to helping caregivers who are on the way to burnout make different decisions. But it is hard for many who believe that they are powerless to set boundaries or be an advocate for themselves. It breaks my heart because burnout is 100 percent preventable. This may seem overly dramatic, but I view caregiver burnout as deciding to commit suicide over a period of time.

It is sad to see good people burn themselves out when it is so preventable. In fact, many of them don't change. They go on to suffer from exhaustion and other health issues that cause them to involuntarily stop their caregiving duties. They eventually end up needing a caregiver themselves. It is so sad to see this happen when it is so avoidable. The bottom line is that caregivers need care too, even if they think they are invincible.

For those who are familiar with the Bible, I will remind you that Philippians 4:13 (NLT) says, "For I can do everything with the help of Christ who gives me the strength I need." God has already given us the power to change into the person we need to become in order to be a great caregiver. He also has given us the power to have the discipline and common sense to take breaks and to put our needs at an equal level as our care-receivers.

Without that discipline, everybody loses. If you are sick or exhausted or emotionally out of control, it's impossible to provide proper care to anyone else.

What Do You Need to Live a Fulfilled, Happy Life?

The *only* way you can successfully care for your loved one without burning out is to, without exception, make certain that *your* needs are met. Period. If you sacrifice yourself, you will be sacrificed. And if you are sacrificed, you will do an inferior job as a long-term caregiver.

If you find yourself arguing with me inside your head right now, I want to remind you that anyone whose needs are not met will suffer, and eventually burn out. There are no good reasons for you to become an emotional, spiritual, or physical casualty due to taking care of your loved one. You must insist that you and your loved one's needs are met so that both of you can live up to your God-given potential. I encourage you to make a commitment to yourself to protect your own life with the same vigor and dedication that you protect your loved one's.

I believe that life should be fun. It might seem odd that I make this statement. I suspect that one of the reasons I've done so well as a long-term caregiver is my insistence on having fun in life, in spite of any or all of the challenges I've faced. It's hard to laugh when you and your loved one are going through such difficult times—but you must. For your sake and for the person you are caring for. Laughter has long proven to be a great healer.

Before we address your loved one's needs in this book, I want to first ask you: "What do you need to have a fulfilled and happy life?" It may surprise you that the first question I encourage you to ask is about your own well-being and life satisfaction. Many of the caregivers I speak with, and most certainly those who are burning out, reject the idea that their lives can be enjoyable and expansive. The daily duties of a caregiver can severely limit your life—*but only if you allow it.* Caregivers burn out because they do not *insist* that their needs are met.

What I am saying may seem harsh, but it's true. I have been my wife's caregiver for decades, and recently for my mother before she passed away. And I thoroughly enjoy my life because I refuse to allow my needs to be overshadowed by those I love. For me to enjoy my life, I need several things. Here is a short, but certainly not an exhaustive list, that will help you protect yourself from burnout. I need to:

- Have time to myself on a daily basis

- Get away for a few days by myself or with friends on occasion

- Go sailing periodically (sailing is where I first met Charlene)

- Have interests that are separate from caregiving

I don't sacrifice the key activities and interests that energize or revitalize me, and you aren't required to sacrifice what makes you happy, either. Before your loved one was dependent upon you for their primary care, your life was full of interesting people and projects. Is your life still that way, or have you assumed you can't have those relationships or adventures any longer?

Don't fret if it seems impossible to rearrange your life to include these activities at this point. We will address this further in the book. The key point now is for you to make a firm commitment to your own well-being.

I will be coming back to this theme repeatedly in the book to remind you that the best way to stay healthy, maintain your own well-being, make the best decisions regarding your loved one and provide the best care is to *enjoy each day*. I'm not suggesting that you pretend to be happy when you're not, or to ignore the difficult feelings or losses. At the risk of sounding a little like a greeting card, I am going to encourage you to *make an attempt* to find joy in every day—in a flower, a beautiful sunset, a silly joke or a simple hug. All we have is right now. Make the moment as fun and beautiful as possible.

Let's Talk About You

Where are you right now on the burnout scale? I like to use this simple quiz from AARP to determine if you are a candidate for caregiver burnout:

1. Do you feel furious one minute, and then sad and helpless the next?

   Less [1] [2] [3] [4] [5] More

2. Do you catch every bug that comes your way?

   Less [1] [2] [3] [4] [5] More

3. Do you find yourself snapping at everyone?

   Less [1] [2] [3] [4] [5] More

4. Do you know you should exercise, but you just don't have the time?

   Less [1] [2] [3] [4] [5] More

5. Can you remember the last time you met a friend for dinner or a movie?

   Less [1] [2] [3] [4] [5] More

6. Are you always the "go-to" caregiver?

   Less [1] [2] [3] [4] [5] More

A score of 24 to 30 means you are either burned out or very close to it.

A score of 13 to 23 means you may be rapidly approaching burnout, but if you act quickly, you might be able to avoid it.

A score of 6 to 12 means that you are most likely

a healthy caregiver; however, if your score is closer to 12 than it is to 6, you may need to begin focusing on putting your needs first a little more often.

(Quiz reprinted with permission from AARP.) For instructions to improve your scores, go to www. CaregiversCaregiver.com/ 671-2.

CHAPTER 3

SAY "YES" TO THE GRIEF PROCESS; SAY "NO" TO DEPRESSION

AFTER CHARLENE'S STROKE, she and I grieved for different things in our own ways. Charlene grieved the loss of her ability to speak in complete sentences. Because she could no longer move her right side, she never expected to be able to cook again, or dress herself, or engage in the many creative projects she had prior to her stroke. We both lost the relationship we'd enjoyed for so many years. She lost her independence and her ability to walk, and if she would have allowed it, she could have even lost her faith. But she chose not to.

I grieved over similar issues, but they weren't identical. I lost my ability to come and go as I pleased. My schedule was more closely linked to

Charlene's needs. Charlene and I haven't had a "normal" conversation since 1996. She is still a great communicator–but she relies on grunts and facial expressions and less than a handful of words that she can still speak. Both of us suffered terrible losses due to her stroke.

Grief is an experience none of us want to suffer. It lets us know that we've lost something or someone dear to us. You and your loved one are both grieving; however, what you've lost is different. Your loved one has experienced the pain of an accident or illness that has robbed them of their physical or mental abilities. Your grief, however, is tied up with watching someone you love suffer. Your body and mind are still intact, but you've lost the life you used to live due to your loved one's current limitations.

The grief process itself tests the relationship between you and your loved one. We all grieve in different ways and at varying speeds. Watching Charlene grieve was extremely painful to experience. The first two years after her stroke were the worst for me, and I suspect for her as well. It is a process of emotions that are predictable and yet uncontrollable. It's critical that you give yourself permission to grieve your way, and allow your loved one to grief in his or her way.

Grief Is a Process

You may have noticed that the appearance of grief's intense emotions is unpredictable. In an effort to be strong for your loved one, you may try to suppress your emotions. Then, out of the blue, a wave of sadness, anger or despair crashes over you–often at times when you least expect them. You may be grocery shopping or driving in the car or watching a television show. Something small sets you off and then the next thing you know, you're sobbing or raging or feeling utterly overwhelmed. You're not crazy. You're grieving, and that's OK. There is no perfect way to grieve.

In the beginning of this nightmare, when my wife was doing speech and physical therapy, we believed that Charlene would recover her lost brain functions quickly. But the days slowly ran into weeks, then months, then years, and now it has been over two decades. We are very grateful that no one told us back then that we would still be affected by this today. There *is* life on the other side of a tragedy of this magnitude. Charlene and I have vibrant lives today–there is hope for a good life, but it will be a *different* life. And the first step is into the grief.

Going through the grieving process was an on-the-job training experience for me. There is a general consensus in the psychological community that agrees with the five stages of the grief process that the Swiss psychologist, Elisabeth Kubler-Ross, studied and wrote about in her book, *On Death and Dying* (1969). Some therapists, however, have added two more phases, while others may have some different names and groupings. Still others may list some stages in a different order. I am focusing on three phases in this chapter: bargaining, anger and depression.

Bargaining

Bargaining—trying to make a deal with others and God—is a normal part of the grieving process. Some of you may have heard of the term "foxhole Christian," referring to a brand new soldier who finds himself in a combat situation with bullets whizzing over his head. He may be grieving the loss of his personal freedom by not being safe at home with his family. He may also be trying to negotiate some kind of bargain with God in his prayers. Maybe he is praying that if God gets him out of this situation alive, he will devote himself to going to church every single Sunday for the rest of his life.

The bargaining stage involves the hope that the individual can somehow undo or avoid a cause of grief. In less traumatic situations, bargaining is sought to negotiate a compromise. For example, in the breakup of a romantic relationship, one may say to the other, "Can we still be friends?" It is rare that bargaining can provide a solution to the causes of grief, as many of them are strictly non-negotiable, such as death.

From the very beginning of Charlene's and my grief process, I tried to convince God to speed up this trial so that we could get on with our lives and start telling the world how He miraculously healed her. Charlene was praying a similar kind of prayer. I often saw her praying and crying in her room with her Bible open. We both, in our own ways, tried to negotiate a relief from our pain and suffering. I prayed, "What if I devoted the rest of my life to helping others? Then can I wake up and realize this has all been a bad dream?"

We became lost in a maze of "if only" or "what if" statements. We wanted life returned to the way it was. I wanted to go back in time, choose the correct hospital, and get the proper medication that would have prevented Charlene's brain trauma. The "if only's" caused us to find fault in ourselves and what we think we could have done differently.

The faith that we had in God was deeply shaken. It is very easy to have faith when all is well, but you discover how much faith you really have when tragedy strikes. We simply did not want to accept this new reality. We believed that God had a purpose in all of this and Charlene would be healed soon.

Our prayers were very selfish bargaining prayers back then, and yet God was always there for us. Even if He didn't answer the prayers the way we wanted, He gave us what we needed instead and helped us get through our challenging trial one day at a time. I know that I felt His presence every single minute.

Some of the ways that God made himself known to Charlene and me during our times of need and confusion was through a number of *His* people who he sent to us. They showed us God's love through their actions and service. Meals were prepared for us at home, pastors came to the house to pray with us, volunteers came to help Charlene so I could go to work, go on errands and do the shopping. Wherever there was a hardship, there was a "saint" who came by to meet that need. It was miraculous. It was *not* a coincidence, because after about a hundred "coincidences" or so, you come to realize that there is no such thing. Our faith became more real than it ever has before. Think about it. You can really tell if you are living by faith *not* when things are going great, but when you are overdrawn in the bank, when the doctor says you have cancer, when your wife hands you divorce papers, when your boss fires you or when your attorney says that bankruptcy is your only option.

We are different people today, and much stronger as a result of God allowing us to go through this grief and this trial. We still believe that God has a purpose in all of this. Maybe it's to tell you our story so that you can get through your grief. There is a verse in the Bible that reveals God's perspective of trials. When the Apostle Paul asked God to remove his "thorn in my flesh" three different times; God did not answer his prayer. He simply told Paul each time, "My grace is all you need. My power works best in weakness." And so Paul declares, "So now I am glad to boast about my weaknesses, so that the power of Christ can work through me" (2 Corinthians 12:9, NLT).

That Scripture specifically spoke to me by assuring me that I wasn't anything special to be going through this trial. *Everybody* is going through something. Yet to realize that the trial we were going through was *custom-tailored* by God just for us was, and still is, mind-blowing. It was not a random occurrence. It was not bad luck. It didn't just happen when God was taking a nap and wasn't watching over us. It was deliberately allowed by our Heavenly Father because He saw something in us that needed more perfection than it already had. He allowed the devil to torment us because he knew that would draw us closer to Him. He knew that a closer relationship with our Creator was worth *any* price to occur, even extreme pain.

I do not ever want to repeat all that has happened to us over the last twenty years, but I also would never want to change the negative experiences that God allowed us to go through. Those experiences made us who we are today: stronger, closer to God, having more faith, acquiring experience to minister to others, compassion, empathy, and just making us better people. It was a heavenly prescription for what we needed at the time but didn't know we needed it. What a mighty God we serve. And let me just state it once more. I would not want to repeat it again for a million dollars, but I also would not want to change any of it for even a *billion* dollars. It was both that painful, and that life-changing for the better.

Anger Releases Pent Up Feelings We Can't Identify

By simply realizing that your loved one is in the anger stage of the grief process, you can exhibit much better control over your own emotions and avoid displaying inappropriate anger toward that person. Even though your loved one may not be in total control of their anger, it's important to hold onto the fact that you are not the cause of their disability or challenge. Take care to protect yourself emotionally from the anger that may be pointed in your direction. This stage of grieving is part of the normal process for your loved one. It is also important that you recognize that your anger is part of your emotional process as well.

There are many different types of anger, but I am going to discuss only a few here. There is righteous anger–anger dealing with the true injustices of the world, the anger that can motivate one to start a movement of change. Martin Luther King is an example of changing social injustice due to racism. There is moral anger–the injustice of watching children starve around the world due to corrupt politics that creates a moral anger to motivate individuals to starting organizations such as Feed the Children or World Vision. There is also passive anger, violent anger, self-inflicted anger, judgmental anger, and many, many more.

The anger of which I'm referring to is a volatile anger, one of pure torment, fear, and frustration. Charlene held a rage within that she could not express in words. She was only able to howl and scream the pain of anguish and loss of her life as she knew it. She felt that falling victim to an impending stroke in her brain was completely unfair.

Anger is a powerful emotion that can be very destructive if not properly channeled. After we had moved on from our bargaining, Charlene and I found ourselves both immersed in our anger. Her vocabulary mainly consisted of very frustrating screams—and scream she did. Emotional outbursts lasted anywhere between fifteen minutes to an hour and consisted of bone-chilling shrieks that did not stop, except to take her next breath to continue howling. The target of her rage was me. My anger was a retaliatory anger that wanted to lash back at the person who was getting me angry. Fortunately, I wasn't always successful at that.

As terrifying as it was for me to see and hear my wife having an emotional meltdown, I had to constantly remind myself that she was communicating the only way that she knew how. I tried holding her, rubbing her back, and talking calmly to her, but nothing helped her to regain her peaceful spirit. The loved one you are caring for may also exhibit extreme outbursts of anger that seem specifically designed to hurt you. It is important to understand that, although their hurt and anger may seem to be targeted at you, it is really the expression of their own inner pain, frustration, fear, and loss.

During this time, it felt like I had no control over my own life. My wife was suffering immeasurably, and I could not comfort her. I was confronted with a myriad of decisions to make on Charlene's behalf (as well as my own), and I had no prior experience with this level of physical disability. The woman who had been my best friend, and upon whom I relied, was gone. I felt alone in my own pain. In that stressed emotional space, I was vulnerable and Charlene's outbursts affected me personally. I often got quite angry with Charlene because of the way she treated me. Charlene's confusion, inner pain, and loss of control of her own life prevented her from understanding the plans I would make on her behalf. I felt as if she did not appreciate all that I was trying to do to make her life better. However, I've learned over the years from personal experience that, no matter how out of control my life seemed at times, I always have power over the way I react to a situation. Granted, many times I did not respond to her livid eruptions as lovingly as I should have.

There were times that she was very angry with me about things I had no control over, like when her driver's license got revoked, which caused me to have to sell her beautiful car. She could not understand that it was the stroke that robbed her of her car—in her mind, it was *me* because *I* did it. It was the same with our beautiful two-story house. She did not understand that it was dangerous to climb stairs when half your body is paralyzed. All she knew was that I was selling our dream home that she loved. It was *me, I* did it, and I paid a heavy price of stress and aggravation from her for these "injustices." I don't even think about those bad times anymore since it just produces negative energy and does not accomplish anything productive. I really had to dig deep into my memory to bring these buried feelings back to life just for this book. But don't worry, I'm sure that I will have no problem burying them again in the dark recesses of my mind where they belong.

Back then, I was not accustomed to such treatment, and I had to constantly remind myself not to take it personally. I told myself that she was sick and could not be held accountable for most of her actions. It was only because of God's grace in me that I chose to express my own anger in more constructive and positive ways. For example, during those frustrating times, I found a way to *safely* vent my anger. I would write her scathing letters, venting my rage and true feelings, just to get them off my chest. I described how she hurt me and how unfair it was that she was treating me this way. These letters were strictly for my benefit. Of course, I would never send them. They are hidden in my filing cabinet, safe from Charlene's eyes. It wouldn't have served any beneficial purpose to anyone; in fact, it would have caused a hurricane in our relationship that we may not have recovered from. This strategy is an excellent way to safely express the rage inside of you without allowing your anger to ever get out of control.

I thank God that I listened to that still, small voice in my head telling me to just love her and not pay attention to any of her words or actions–that it was just her grief and anger talking. I had to continually remind myself not to take these offenses personally because my wife was not in her right mind. After all, if I was not in my right mind, wouldn't I want my caregiver and spouse to extend this same grace to me?

It was impossible for my wife to participate in any intense, verbal conversation of any kind about any deep topic on any level because of the speech impairment resulting from her stroke. She simply was not capable of effectively expressing the profound emotions she was feeling. Since most passionate "conversations" became a one-sided shouting match, neither of us felt heard or understood. Having a difficult conversation with a loved one who is fully functional is challenging enough, but can you imagine how it would turn out with one who is severely speech-impaired? Anger will only heighten the emotions and negatively affect the desired outcome of your communication. It's very unproductive to attempt any meaningful conversation in the heat of rage. Wait for those intense emotions to subside before continuing with the dialogue.

It would invariably take a tremendous amount of energy for Charlene to vent in that way, and it would usually take her many days to fully recover from those outbursts. It drained her body and her emotions. Sometimes I felt that those outbursts were my fault for allowing our conversations to reach a point of so much frustration that she would just snap. She couldn't stop herself once she got started. It had to run its course. I don't know—maybe I'm just being a martyr for wanting to take some of the blame for those outbursts. After all, I know that she has *very* limited communication skills since her stroke, so it isn't really fair for me to bring up topics (even if they are very important topics) that I know she won't be able to calmly and patiently be able to express herself adequately enough to prove her arguments. These are always difficult calls for me. I usually think that I *have* to bring up a particular topic because it is so very important, and I am usually optimistic that she can handle discussing it. But then thirty seconds into the conversation,

I realize that I've just made a terrible mistake, and was incorrect in assuming that we could have a productive exchange. The emotional drain on her after these outbursts, in my opinion, is simply not worth discussing these kind of topics (such as why we had to move, or sell her house and car, or why I went to New York to visit a relative without her when I was suffering from burnout, etc.).

Of course, she will always disagree with me on this topic of discussing difficult subjects. She *always* wants to get into these discussions with me even though they are usually destined for disaster because she is optimistic that she can handle them, but it usually is the exception rather than the rule. A recent topic we can't seem to agree on is the gardener; Charlene wants to discuss all the wrong things he does. I, on the other hand, think he is doing a good job trying to follow her instructions. Again, many of these conversations are absolutely necessary because they usually involve changes that need to be implemented in our living arrangements. I give her my reasons. Typically, she doesn't agree but can't articulate why. When I sense that she is heading toward another emotional outburst, I stop the conversation and change the subject.

As the caregiver, it's important to take the high road and understand that the angry person you are caring for is not behaving rationally. I'll be the first one to admit that understanding this doesn't necessarily make it any easier to deal with. But it may help if you put yourself in your care-receiver's place by imagining what they are going through.

In my wife's case, I imagine myself attempting to discuss something very important yet not being able to say a word. I imagine that, by losing an argument with my spouse, I may lose something very valuable to me because I wasn't able to articulate my case or speak my mind well enough. (It's similar to an attorney losing a very important and winnable case because he failed to convince the jury as a result of inadequate articulation). I start to feel empathy toward her after these exercises, which is a very important emotion for a caregiver to possess.

The ability to communicate verbally with each other is a significant part of humanity that most of us take for granted. For reasons unknown to me, this was taken away from my wife. Likewise, your care-receiver has suffered some sort of loss that was very precious to them. It may be their health, their mind, their mobility, their speech, their understanding, or even their youth. For this and many other reasons, empathy and compassion are essential ingredients for caregiving; this allows you to *feel* their pain. Although there is no guarantee that this will fix anything, at least your loved one will sense that you are trying to understand and empathize with them, even if you still have to do things that they do not like.

Sometimes the anger stage lasts a little longer than expected, and this may require you to take some extra breaks away from your loved one in order to survive caregiving. As I mentioned above, one way that I attempted to endure those difficult days was to travel out of state on selected weekends to some of my favorite friends or family members' homes. I hadn't seen many of them in years, and it was a special treat for me just to get away from reality and share my frustrations with wonderful people in a safe place without feeling guilty for doing so.

That's not to say that taking breaks were easy to arrange. Anyone who suffers a stroke or any disability is naturally self-absorbed with their own problems, and Charlene was no exception. My wife was not happy about me leaving. I know a lot of caregivers who cannot say "No" to their loved one when they disagree on whose needs should be taken care of first (even though a happy caregiver usually means a happy loved one). To neglect this concept means the care-receiver will typically fall short on the level of care they receive because their caregiver is carrying too heavy of a load to give their best. The goal here is to take care of your needs so that you won't be in survival mode. It is important to "teach" your loved one that, as difficult as it may seem at times, they must be able to handle the truth, or else you may find it very tempting to stretch the truth or even worse, to lie to them.

I can imagine some of you are asking me right now, "How can I get away and find someone to care for my loved one for a whole weekend?" Of course, you'll need someone who can provide *adequate* care while you are gone. Obviously, no one will be able to provide the *same* excellent level of attention that you offer, but that's OK. Your loved one will certainly appreciate you more when you get back from your trip. At any rate, you will be able to be a *better* caregiver if you follow these words of wisdom.

Sadness

It's easy to mistake depression for sadness, but they actually are very different. If you confuse these two emotions, you may respond to your feelings in a way that *increases* your chances of burnout, rather than lessens it.

Sadness or sorrow is part of the *natural* grieving process. Clinical depression, however, is not. Sadness is a "normal" emotion that we all share when something difficult occurs, we lose something or someone we love or we're disappointed and hurt. We may be sad because a pet has gone missing, a job was lost or, in the case of this book's topic, a loved one became ill or injured. Sadness disappears once the situation changes for the better. If we find our lost dog, we're no longer sad. If we find a new job, we're ready to move on. And once we adjust to the changes in our lives as caregivers, our basic sense of happiness returns.

Clinical depression, however, is a chemical imbalance in our brain chemistry that is not natural or normal. We're not sad about something; we're depressed about everything. It's like living with a gray film over our lives. We're depleted of energy, hope and the ability to solve problems effectively. While sadness comes into our lives for a period of time, depression can go on for weeks, months, and even years. Many people who *feel sorrowful* mistake that feeling for depression, which causes the confusion of why they don't feel better after the situation improves.

If you feel sad because of the difficulties you're

facing, there's no need to be alarmed. You have suffered losses and stresses, and it's natural to experience sorrow. However, if you see yourself as getting stuck in the dark feelings, it's critical that you get professional help. Short-term use of antidepressant medication can be of great benefit to you at this time. Once the proper chemistry in your brain is restored, you may no longer need medication.

Let me emphasize this for you. If you are depressed, it's extremely difficult to restore your balance without therapy and/or proper medication. Hopelessness is a symptom of depression, so it can be hard for those in depression to believe that anyone or anything can help them.

If you are reluctant to ask for help, then consider that a sign that you are depressed rather than sad. People going through a natural part of the grief process have hope and are able to make use of assistance. Some disabilities, however, like stroke or trauma to the brain, can actually cause a chemical imbalance that requires medication in a person who may have *never suffered* from clinical depression before.

Let's Talk About You

It's very important for you to accurately assess your own feelings if you want to avoid burnout. Depression is a serious condition that will likely get worse if you ignore or deny it. Here are some distinctions between sadness and depression that can help you determine if you need assistance:

Sadness: About something
Depression: About everything

Sadness: Crying, talking, taking time alone, praying and other activities relieve the pain
Depression: Nothing helps to relieve the pain.

Sadness: Sleep may be temporarily disrupted. After sleep, you feel rested and rejuvenated.
Depression: Insomnia and the inability to fall or stay asleep is common. In spite of sleep, you still feel tired and depleted.

If you suspect that you are struggling with depression, don't take it lightly. I've found that it's challenging for depressed people to reach out for help—they feel so helpless that they have lost hope. There is hope for you and it's available *if you ask for it*. Please contact a close friend you trust, a pastor or other spiritual leader, or a therapist to get the help you need and deserve.

CHAPTER 4

SAY "YES" TO QUALITY CARE;
SAY "NO" TO PERFECTIONISM

I'LL ADMIT THAT I believe no one can take care of Charlene as well as I can. We've been together for so many years now, before and after her stroke, and I love her beyond measure. I know what she likes and doesn't like. I understand what her words and facial expressions mean. When we're together, I am at peace knowing that she is getting the best possible care.

At the same time, I also know that when I am weary and my own needs are sacrificed, I can become short-tempered and impatient. I'm not as sympathetic to her feelings, not because I no longer care, but because there are limits to what any human being can do for another. Sometimes my best care isn't as perfect as I'd like.

IT'S MY LIFE, TOO!

Say "Yes" to Quality Care

Because I know that my ability to care for Charlene depends first on my ability to care for myself, I have learned that "good enough is good enough." I am not the only person in the world who can give Charlene proper care. Yes, I see myself as the "best" caregiver (which may be a bit egotistical, I'll admit). But *adequate* care is *acceptable* care if that is the only care that is available–even though it can be a bit of a struggle for the perfectionist inside of me.

Quality care is not perfect care but, then again, perfection isn't obtainable. And quality care is more than adequate for your loved one when you need to be assured that your needs are met as well. Let's start by focusing on your loved one's needs.

Identifying Your Loved One's Legitimate Needs

The more aware you are of your loved one's needs, the better able you will be to assure that they are met. The more concrete you can be about your role as a caregiver, the more likely you will be able to provide or to oversee the provision of quality care. Without clear expectations, it is easy for a caregiver to feel as if their job never ends. If you believe your loved one's needs are limitless, you will set yourself up to fail–because you are not limitless. If you write out their specific needs, with a realistic schedule so that you can plan ahead, it will help you realize that your loved one's needs are not infinite. They are finite and doable. At the end of this chapter is an exercise that will help you identify legitimate needs.

The best result comes when you and your loved one co-create a list of expectations. When you can both mutually agree on this list, there is a much higher chance of happiness and a sense of well-being for you and your loved one. If you are dealing with a young child, or someone with a brain injury or other debilitating illness, coming to an agreement may not be possible. But to the best of your ability, empower your loved one to participate in setting the schedule and identifying what is needed. You can both check off items from a to-do list or follow a set schedule that can give a sense of accomplishment, as well as create an atmosphere of safety and satisfaction. If, however, you and your loved one cannot agree on their needs and your role in meeting those needs, conflict, disappointment ,and frustration will be the likely outcome.

One of the biggest mistakes I see caregivers make is assuming that if their loved ones are happy, they are receiving proper care. Many people who burn out as caregivers have a rather vague idea of what their loved ones actually need. Instead of having clear and measurable goals, you may try to meet *all* needs—whether it is in their best interest or not. You may be tempted to assume that as long as your loved one is happy, you've done your job.

The fact is, your loved one's "happiness" is not a true indicator of their legitimate needs. Let's get very honest with each other. Your loved one, if they are like most other "normal" people, probably wants your undivided attention. Their sense of happiness can shift from moment to moment, depending on a variety of things, such as how effectively they deal with their own emotional life, the level of pain they may be experiencing, or the impact of drugs in their system. There may be times when your loved one does not want to follow through with the doctor's instructions, and your insistence on providing them with the care they need may trigger anger, resistance or other unhappy responses. Your loved one may be thrilled if you let him or her off the hook, but doing so would not be providing top quality care. One's emotional state at a particular moment does not determine one's legitimate needs for care.

A burned-out caregiver is often the one who is being "run ragged" trying to make their loved one happy. Yes, your loved one faces challenges, but it is important to realize that everyone has challenges, no matter what their circumstances. It is not your responsibility, nor is it in your power, to keep your loved one happy. How he or she responds to life is up to them. Your job is to make sure that their legitimate needs are met–by you or by someone else.

As you create a clear description of your loved one's needs, you may discover there is less for you to do than you had suspected. Or, in some cases, your loved one may require the presence of someone around the clock. The key element is identifying, in measureable terms, the exact nature of these needs.

Identifying What Your Loved One Can Do Independently

Most caregivers burn out because of their giving, self-sacrificial and compassionate natures. However, we may be tempted to do more than our loved ones actually need, or intervene when it would be best for them to learn how to care for themselves. Without realizing it, we may impede our loved one's progress by being overly protective. If you always help your loved one do the things that they find difficult to do instead of encouraging them to try harder, it can make them more dependent than necessary. You may discourage the extra efforts of doing it themselves, robbing them of a sense of self mastery and confidence.

After my wife's stroke, Charlene's mother came

to live with us to help out with the caregiving responsibilities. Her mother was a very good caregiver with a great deal of experience taking care of both her parents and her mother-in-law as they became sicker with the onset of age. However, there are different types of caregiving styles that may not be appropriate to your loved one's needs. Her mother was one type and I was another. Her mother would often get things for Charlene if she was struggling to get them, especially if it was *not* occupational therapy time, or if Charlene was not particularly in the mood for any therapy.

I was told by an occupational therapist that the best kind of caregiving is where you help the patient to learn to do things for themselves as opposed to always coming to their rescue when they are struggling for something. In essence, I believed that occupational therapy should happen not only when scheduled, but when any suitable opportunity arises.

Charlene's mother often grabbed something for her that she was struggling to reach in the cupboard, whereas I would say something like, "Come on, you can do it. Stretch a little more, you can reach it. You're almost there." I could tell that at times Charlene did *not* appreciate my "encouragement" as it would have been easier in the moment for me to just giver her what she wanted like her mom would. Charlene was grateful for the extra help that she got from her mother, while I usually got dirty looks from both of them, especially when she wasn't particularly in the mood. But in the long run, it helped her to become the very independent person she is today.

For example, her mother volunteered to cook all of the meals and thought that Charlene couldn't or shouldn't have to cook because of her paralysis. However, I believed that my wife loved being the gourmet cook that she had been, and I wanted her to regain that pleasure in life. Charlene agreed. Because she is an amazingly determined woman, and due to my "encouraging" her to do whatever she could for herself, Charlene now cooks all our meals and prepares dinner parties regularly for close friends and family. It is certainly more difficult, and it takes a great deal more time to cook since her disability. However, she does it—and does it very well. She loves cooking, and it gives her another purpose in life: making people happy by feeding them great food. This is one aspect of her life before her stroke that she can continue doing (not the *same* way, but the *new normal* way).

She also does all the housework: sewing, cleaning, laundry, decorating, and organizing. In fact, I can't think of anything that she cannot do, which is amazing, considering she only has use of one arm, one leg, and only a handful of words. I know her recovery would have been negatively affected if things had always been made easy for her, and if I didn't have that "selfish" streak that sometimes a caregiver needs in order to survive.

Say "No" to Perfectionism

I talk with caregivers all of the time, and there is one indicator that allows me to predict whether or not they will, with near certainty, become a burnout casualty. The more of a perfectionist a person is, the more likely burnout will occur. That might surprise you, but I've seen time and time again how perfectionists unwittingly make decisions that set them up for stress-related illnesses, emotional overwhelm and a joyless life.

Perfectionists are never satisfied. Since no one is perfect, it's impossible to satisfy a perfectionist—not even themselves. I've met so many caregivers who are ruthless to themselves, never feeling like what they've done is enough. A heavy cloud of failure, self-criticism and dissatisfaction hangs over their heads. I promise you—if you hold yourself to a perfectionistic standard, you will (sooner rather than later) be burned to a crisp.

Will your loved one do everything as well as you could? Perhaps, but probably not. Will they be as quick as you might be? It's doubtful. But when they take care of themselves, you give them the opportunity to feel better about their lives and more engaged with activities that make life worth living.

Rather than have patience and allow your loved one to go according to their own time table and abilities, it's tempting to do everything yourself. What is the hurry? Why not relax and encourage your loved one, rather than criticize them or rob them of more independence? When your loved one can regain some of their own independence, you both win. Your life is easier, and your loved one receives the confidence and competency they feared was lost.

The stress and confusion perfectionism causes can really hamper your effectiveness to be a great caregiver, especially if you are the type of person who: is easily offended, is overly sensitive, is anxious to please people, finds confrontation difficult, is easily taken advantage of, is too passively introverted, or already has a weak self-image of themselves. In essence, caregiving is not for wimps or weaklings. You must be strong, have thick skin, and be assertive and confident in your caregiving role while realizing the importance of taking care of yourself first.

Tough love–a necessary part of protecting

yourself–can appear mean or selfish to others. Only you can decide if you're acting out of anger or selfishness. When you have a clear description of your loved one's legitimate needs, everyone involved can see whether or not quality care is being provided. But I've never met anyone who wants to be told "No." When we set boundaries that protect ourselves, while assuring quality care is provided, you can know that you are truly giving your best.

I realize that some loved ones are bedridden and do not have any physical or occupational therapy that you may supervise or help them with. In fact, the bedridden care-receivers can be more demanding with their inability to do things for themselves. You may have to let them know, for example, that "between the hours of 12 and 2, I will be taking a break, so please allow me to serve you before and after that. Otherwise I won't be available unless it is an emergency." This is a much better policy than allowing yourself to be on call 24/7.

Remember, any of us can become self-centered and find it easy to rely on others to fulfill all our needs. Remember, *It's Your Life, Too!* The world does not revolve around your loved one–there's room for all of us. I may sound harsh, but if you don't speak up and establish a healthy boundary, then resentment will build. As you experience burnout, you'll miss legitimate signs of distress and run the risk of being disrespectful, short-tempered, and insensitive.

In the next chapter, we're going to explore how you can get more help in meeting the needs of your loved one. It's not simply up to the two of you. Before you can ask for help, it's important for you to determine what needs to be done.

Let's Talk About You

Exercise: Make a List of Your Loved One's Needs

Medical Care:

- Calling Doctors and Picking Up Prescriptions from the Pharmacy
- Managing Delivery or Pick Up of Supplies and Equipment
- Administering Prescriptions and Care
- Overseeing Medication Schedule
- Provision of Specific Treatment (such as breathing treatments, blood sugar monitoring, dressing at surgery site, etc.
- Symptom and/or Pain Management

Treatment Care:

- Keeping Track of Appointments
- Transportation to Appointments

- Helping to Communicate with Doctors and Other Care Providers
- Helping with Therapy Homework

Personal Care and Hygiene

- Dressing
- Bathing
- Grooming
- Toileting
- Massages

Home-Based Activities:

- Cooking
- House Cleaning
- Bed-making
- Laundry
- Grocery and Other Shopping
- Errands of Various Types
- Pet Care and Feeding

Supervision and Mobility:

- Continuum: Weekly Visitation–Round the Clock
- Companionship
- Assistance with Walking
- Scheduling and Overseeing Home Care
- Physical Therapy

- Occupational Therapy
- Visiting Nurse
- Social Worker
- Other

Financial Management:

- Paying Bills
- Handling Insurance
- Maintaining Bank Account
- Collecting Retirement and Social Security
- Will and Estate Planning

Emotional Well-Being:

- Coordinating Friends and Family Visits
- Assistance in Attending Church or Community Groups
- Companionship
- Providing Transportation for Attending Events and Support Groups

CHAPTER 5

SAY "YES" TO BOUNDARIES;
SAY "NO" TO LIMITLESS CAREGIVING

WE LIVE IN a world of boundaries. They are essential to basic life. Caregiving is no different. A simple trip to the store would not be possible without clear boundaries that are set, understood and respected by everyone. The doors of your car are designed so that we know where and how to get in. We don't all pile into a car, sitting wherever we want. Instead, the driver has a special seat and passengers have their spots as well. As a final reminder of who sits where, seat belts have been installed for each passenger and, by law, must be used.

A driveway is designed and built with boundaries—most of us do not park on our lawns or on the sidewalk, but in our driveways. These are designed to slope into the street, which is further marked by curbs. In many streets, painted lines let us know where is it lawful and safe to drive . . . and in which direction.

After we pull into the shopping center parking lot, we find that lines have been painted on the pavement to show us where we ought to park– boundaries that make it possible for a large number of people to come and go without incident. Crosswalks are marked; doors are built for entering and exiting. I could go on, but I'm sure you get the idea. Without boundaries, everyday life would be chaotic. And in some countries, where laws are unclear and infrastructure is in disarray, life is extremely difficult and haphazard. And yet, when it comes to relationships, many caregivers view boundaries as mysterious, difficult, or unnecessary. As a consequence, these relationships are often troubled or turbulent, with people feeling violated, resentful or misunderstood. The healthiest relationships, and therefore the most enjoyable and fulfilling, are those with clear, agreed-upon boundaries. This fact is all the more important in relationships between caregivers and care-receivers.

In most situations, you and your loved one had

a previous relationship that was in place prior to the illness, accident or whatever limited their ability to be more independent. If your past relationship was a healthy one, based in clear communication and honored boundaries, then you will be more capable of renegotiating the boundaries in this new situation. However, even in the best of circumstances, the change is usually so abrupt and/ or so significant, that the changes in expectations and roles are difficult to re-establish. This was very challenging for me and Charlene at the beginning— and continues to be as our individual needs change with aging.

Boundaries Are Based on What We Need

In previous chapters, you have identified what you need to live a fulfilling life as well as the legitimate needs of your loved one. Think of boundaries as the tools by which you both have your needs met—the rules of your relationship, so to speak. In the same way that you are expected to drive on the right side of the street and park in the proper spots in a lot, you and your loved one must agree upon the same rules and expectations for there to be harmony in your lives.

Let's be honest—most of us simply want what we

want, and negotiating boundaries is hard work. Like infants who are mindful solely of their own needs, it's easy for caregiver and care-receiver alike to be more aware of their own needs and overlook the needs of the other. I was told by the doctors and staff at the hospital my wife stayed at that a stroke can change the personality of that person. Someone who was very giving and selfless can all of a suddenly become self-centered because they can no longer rely on their independence to feel comfortable about who they are. In essence, the world now revolves around them, and they have no problem letting you know.

Because of the trauma your loved one has suffered, it is understandable that your care-receiver has heightened concern for their own well-being. Without meaning to, your loved one can be like a person drowning in a lake who is so desperate that both the swimmer and the life guard are taken under. I remember those early days in the hospital when Charlene was in extreme physical and emotional pain right after her stroke. I naively tried to "fix" her pain, as is my custom, by putting an anti-spasm balm on her cramping leg, but it ended up making the cramping worse, which made me feel really bad because of the extra suffering that I had inflicted upon her. Just when I felt that things couldn't get any worse, she turned on me and became very, very angry and was verbally abusive in front of all the staff. Of course I couldn't understand her words, but the tonality and fascial expressions were enough for me to never do that again. People at the hospital watched this happen, and I was very embarrassed. I felt like a total idiot, like the person rescuing a drowning victim. But instead, I felt like I needed the rescuing.

Remind yourself that you've made a commitment to providing top quality care to your loved one—you did not agree to become a slave to their every whim and desire. Boundaries are meant to provide for our legitimate needs, not everything we might desire or want at the moment. If you allow this, your loved one may come to believe that it is OK to be overly selfish and be unaware of how harmful or destructive it is to you. And the opposite is true as well—you must be mindful to the vulnerable state your loved one is in and make sure that their needs (which might be quite different from yours) are also met.

Start with a Schedule

One way I recommend that people start a conversation about the new boundaries in their relationship is through the creation of a schedule.

Like roads and parking lots that guide our cars to shopping malls, a daily schedule can guide activities and expectations. The schedule should include your activities as well as your care-receiver.

Start with four events that happen every day:

- Waking up
- Going to sleep
- Eating
- Medication, if applicable

You and your loved one may have different sleep cycles, so indicate when you both rise and go to bed. Set specific times for breakfast, lunch, dinner and snacks. You may be tempted to let this happen "whenever" you or your loved one is hungry. However, the result of this arrangement is you being "on call" 24/7. One of our goals is to make sure you have time for your needs to be met. If you can't plan ahead, then how can you be sure that your needs will be considered?

In addition, put the medications needed in your schedule. You may have a separate chart for tracking meds. That's fine—but I still encourage you to put medications in your shared daily planner.

Here is an example:

Sample Daily Schedule for Adult and Senior Caregivers

Date: _____/_____/_____

12:00 (a.m.) _____

1:00_____

2:00_____

3:00_____

4:00_____

5:00_____

6:00_____

7:00_____

8:00_____

9:00_____

10.00_____

11:00_____

12:00 (noon)_____

1:00_____

2:00_____

3:00_____

4:00_____

5:00_____

6:00_____

7:00_____

8:00_____

9:00_____

10:00_____

11:00_____

Medication Prompting

This is especially helpful when a new doctor or hospital wants to know all the meds your loved one is on. This way they are all at your fingertips.

Medication: _____

Dose: _____

Scheduled times to take: _____

Prescribing doctor: _____

Additional notes about medication (take with food, etc.):

_____

_____

Medication: _____

Dose: _____

Scheduled times to take: _____

Prescribing doctor: _____

Additional notes about medication (take with food, etc.):

_____

_____

Medication: _____

Dose: _____

Scheduled times to take: _____

Prescribing doctor: _____

Additional notes about medication (take with food, etc.):

_____

_____

You now have a basic plan for the day—with boundaries built right in. This might not seem like much of an accomplishment; however, it is. You now have a template that others can use to know what to do, how to do it, and when to do it. That is called delegation and freedom to the primary caregiver, words you will learn to love. These tasks will seem less daunting to someone providing respite to you when they see how organized and easy it is to follow the schedule. If, for example, you are involved in your work or something you enjoy doing, and your loved one asks you to make a meal, you can refer to the schedule and say something like, "If you're really hungry, I'll be glad to get you a snack, but I am busy right now and will get you lunch on time as we agreed." That may or may not go over well, but with the schedule, you have a set boundary. If it turns out that the time for lunch is too late, then the time can be reset for earlier in the day. No drama. No tension. Just a schedule that lets everyone know what will happen and when.

Boundaries Are Not a Secret

One of the issues I see again and again with caregivers is the "unspoken" boundary. The caregiver feels resentful or violated but has never told the care-receiver about the boundary they'd like to set. How can a person honor a boundary they know nothing about?

Perhaps you don't feel appreciated for all that you do because your loved one rarely says the words, "thank you." Your loved one may assume that you know how much your care means to them, but are unaware how much hearing those words mean to you. Your building resentment could be eliminated by a simple conversation. If you let your loved one know that hearing "thank you" is something you need, a boundary you need to set, he or she may be happy to oblige.

However, if your loved one continues to be

unappreciative of your assistance, you may need to take a stronger stand. It's not appropriate for you to withhold what your loved one needs in order to get the appreciation you want. You can set out consequences for their lack of regard, though—such as spending less time in the room (as long as they don't physically require your presence). The example I am using is not a serious one to most caregivers. But I do know of situations where the care-receiver is demanding, disrespectful, and difficult. In these cases, clear boundaries with consequences are required. Otherwise you will grow more and more resentful and be more likely to burn out.

This reminds me of a funny story about a husband whose wife feels that he never tells her he loves her anymore. She finally puts her foot down and demands, "Don't you love me anymore? You never say *I love you!*"

He barks back at her while still reading his newspaper, "I told you that when I married you fifty years ago, if anything changes, I'll let you know." Many times, caregivers are like that wife who just needs to hear it again—and frequently.

Failure to establish boundaries will result in the caregiver feeling taken advantage of, not appreciated, and disrespected. Feelings of resentment, bitterness, and depression may follow and may negatively affect the relationship. The caregiver may become stressed and resent their caregiving responsibilities. Eventually, the care-receiver may receive inadequate care, less respect, and even develop disdain for their loved one (familiarity breeds contempt). This is not a road that anybody wants to go down, especially when it is so simple to establish some ground rules in advance. And then they must be enforced, because they will be tested.

And always remember, the *caregiver* really does hold all the "aces," so to speak. Many used to have all the power in the caregiving relationship, yet they unknowingly handed it over to their disabled loved one. That's like the parent who allows their five-year-old to have the "run the house" with no discipline and now the parents no longer have control over all that goes on at home or in public.

Baby elephants are trained to stay put with a skinny little cord tied to one foot and staked into the ground. Yet they only try to pull that stake up a few times and then give up forever. When the elephant is enormous, the trainers still stake them with a thin cord tied to its foot, because they know that the elephant will never try to get away, since they tried years ago, when they were not that strong. An elephant *never* forgets. They just never realize that they can snap that cord like a piece of thread if they only lifted their leg. The moral of both stories? Without meaning to disrespect your loved one, I use these silly stories to remind you that you are much stronger than you think, and you have all the power on your side, so don't give it away, but instead use it to establish healthy boundaries with your loved one.

When Boundaries Are Difficult to Set

Boundaries may come easily to certain types of personalities but are very difficult for others. People-pleasers and those who dislike confrontation will struggle to implement boundaries. They would rather be offended and be taken advantage of than confront their loved one with reasonable rules to insure the health of the relationship. I am very fortunate to have been blessed with a temperament that makes boundary setting very easy. I am not afraid of confrontation. People always know where they stand with me (and my boundaries). However, I know others that are not so lucky. They resist confrontation like one would resist a root canal. It will be difficult (but not impossible) for these people to learn the art of constructive confrontation and negotiation to implement essential boundaries in their lives for their ultimate survival.

My message to you is this: *It's Your Life, Too!* I encourage you to get over your timidity and become more assertive. Take classes or seminars if needed. Attend a codependent or enabler's meeting like the ones that Alcoholics Anonymous or recovery groups offer. The benefits will be lifelong. You will learn to change your unhealthy habits and acquire new traits that will benefit all your relationships in life.

Healthy emotional and physical boundaries are the basis of healthy relationships. It is important that the care-receiver understands what is allowed in the relationship and what will not be tolerated. This is where it can get very sticky, especially if the relationship is a family member or loved one.

There are many books and blogs out there to help you improve relationships with family members, and these can be very helpful to your caregiving relationship and the healthy boundaries you must establish. It is not likely that your loved one's habits will change; however, your responses to their bad habits can change. The bottom line is that your care-receiver desperately needs you, and that should give you an edge when dealing with any conflict. If you do it with love and respect, the only weapon they would still have is attempting to make you feel guilty. The proper way to deal with guilt will be dealt with in a future chapter.

According to a recent Gallup poll, only half of all Americans are satisfied with their family life and relationships. Is it no wonder, then, that caregivers would also be subject to the same problems with their relationships, especially with their care-receivers? Taken from the Intermountain Healthcare Blog Network, here are some simple things you can do to facilitate happy and healthy relationships in your family, which should also improve your relationship with your care-receivers:

- Communicate with each other. Talk to your partner and children regularly about their dreams, hopes, and aspirations. Ask them engaging questions about their lives and get to know what makes them tick.

- Have meals together. Find a meal each day, or at least a few times a week, that everyone can get together for. Make something that everyone likes and facilitate discussions between family members.

- Have one-on-one time with each family member. Spend time with each family member individually. Go for a walk or play a game. It's as simple as asking what they would like to do for a half hour.

- Schedule family time each week. It's important to make time for the family to do something once a week together. In the digital age it's easy to become distracted and distanced from your family. Take the time to go to a child's soccer meet as a family or go get ice cream together.

- Protect your alone time. Being around your partner and kids all the time can be overwhelming. Don't forget to take some time for yourself each week doing something you enjoy, especially during the summer when the kids are home.

Let's Talk About You

Here is a standard of self-care that I recommend. You can modify this for more time to nurture yourself but I hope you don't decrease the time. (A few of these activities will overlap with some of the tips that I mentioned above):

Once a Day:

- Time to be alone to gather your own thoughts and be free of responsibility (thirty minutes)

- One activity that is not related to caregiving such as a phone call with a friend, watching a favorite television show, taking a bubble bath or some other fun activity.

Once a Week:

- At least one outside activity. It can be lunch, coffee in the afternoon or a dinner with a friend. Make an appointment at the nail salon, get a one- or two-hour massage, read a good book at Starbucks while sipping your favorite brew, go to a movie with a friend or by yourself. . . . You get the idea.

- A full day off to do whatever you please. You will need to arrange full coverage from dawn to bedtime, but this is something you really need. God rested on the Sabbath, and it's foolhardy to think you can go indefinitely without a break. If you can spend the night somewhere else, that is the best, but even if it's simply a full-day outing, it's a must each week.

- A special event with your loved one. This can be a date night, if your care-receiver is your partner, or a trip to the movies or any other activity that disrupts the daily routine for the purpose of joy.

Once a Month

- A getaway of at least one night and two days. If you have the funds, check into a hotel and lavish yourself with pampering. If not, make plans to visit a friend.

CHAPTER 6

SAY "YES" TO TEAM BUILDING; SAY "NO" TO ISOLATION

SINCE I WAS Charlene's husband, everyone assumed that I would become her primary caregiver. I shared that assumption and took on that role without hesitation. But I see myself, not as the sole provider of Charlene's care, but as the coordinator of her care. If you define your role in this same way, you'll see your life from a new vantage point.

From Caregiver to Care-Coordinator

We use the term "caregiver" in our society to mean a great many things, ranging from informal aides to professionals who assist people of all ages. I use the term in defining myself as the Caregiver's Caregiver. My hope is to help other caregivers avoid burnout while living exciting and fulfilling lives. But let's take a closer look at the term to see how it might set us up for burnout.

If we see ourselves as the sole giver of care, then it's natural for us to feel solely responsible for meeting all aspects of our loved ones' lives. We must be chief cook and bottle washer, medicine provider, transporter, bather, dresser, companion, entertainer ... the list is endless. No one is capable of fulfilling all of these roles. Not only is this a misunderstanding of one's calling, it's impossible to meet all the needs of any other human being. It simply can't be done. If you try, you will burn out.

But if you see yourself as the point person, the coordinator of your loved one's care, then a great load is lifted off of your shoulders. It's no longer your responsibility to meet your loved one's needs by yourself. Your task is to build a team of people who meet your loved one's needs, while making sure your needs are met as well.

I discovered in my own life, and while talking with many other caregivers, that taking on this new perspective is challenging. Here are some things that block us from getting the support we need.

Get Over Your Pride

Since I believed that it was my job to take care of Charlene, I thought it was a sign of weakness or failure if I asked for help. Looking back on this now, I am stunned at how ridiculous I acted. How could I have thought I was capable of such a task? No one can be a long-term caregiver all by themselves. And yet, so many of the people I work with buy into that delusion. And it *is* a delusion—because we over-estimate our human limitations and set ourselves up for failure.

As I mentioned in a previous chapter, my wife's mother (and her husband) moved in with us to help with Charlene's care. I am very thankful for the assistance, and I don't know how we would have made it without her. But at the beginning, I felt like their help was required because I was inadequate for the job. It took a lot of pride-swallowing on my part to ask them to move in with us. I've gotten over that. When I need help from other people, I ask for it. If this is a problem for you, you need to get over it too. For example, I hated to ask for help with certain things that I hated doing, like the shopping. Charlene likes to shop—no, she *loves* to shop. She can spend five hours at the grocery store, while I can only take about an hour or two before I go bananas and need to lie down. So I asked some friends who also love to shop to take her. However, it turns out that she wore them all out, and so far, no one can do five hours in the supermarket either. As a result, no one seems to offer to take her shopping anymore, so now it's me again that takes her.

Let me be brutally honest here—if you let your pride get in the way of creating a team of people who will help you care for your loved one, it could kill you. Dramatic? Not really. Let this statistic sink in: 30 percent of caregivers die before the person they are taking care of. Thirty percent! Burnout is deadly, and if your ability to function is compromised, or you become ill yourself, who will provide for your loved one? And if you're dead, well . . . that speaks for itself.

The power over whether or not you burn out as a caregiver and perhaps die prematurely is completely in your hands. You hold all the cards. Only you can (and must) set up boundaries and realistic expectations for yourself that will ensure you are around to care for the one you love. Don't let pride or a false sense of humility set you up for illness and failure. You are a wonderful human being who has chosen to take care of your loved one. But remember, you are only a human being. No more.

Identify What You Need from Your Team

Not everyone who volunteers to help will be needed, and not everyone who is needed may volunteer. So, from the beginning, stake your claim as Team Leader. In previous chapters, I identified what you need to live well and be happy and the specific needs your loved one has as well. The next step is to design a plan that makes sure all of these needs are met—and they cannot all be met by you.

You may be an excellent cook or accustomed to cleaning your own home. That's wonderful. But under these new circumstances, you may need to have someone else do the shopping and meal prep and come in regularly to do laundry and clean the house. Being a caregiver means accepting change to your normal routines; rather than being the only person who takes your loved one to appointments or shopping, plan to have someone else take on this responsibility. Remember what we discussed about perfectionism? It's most likely that you are able to provide the best care for your loved one. But other people can provide top quality care as well. They may do it differently than you, but it will be adequate for the situation. It may even be what is missing.

Identify all of the tasks that other people could

do instead of you. You may not find someone to fulfill these tasks, but at this point, I want you to see that there are just a few items that only you can provide. You are needed—don't get me wrong. But you are needed as a long-term caregiver.

Make a List of Everyone Who Can and Will Help

There are two kinds of people who can help you—volunteers (those who will help for free out of a sense of caring or responsibility) and paid assistants (those who do this for a living.) If you're like us, there's no money growing on the trees in your backyard. But even on a tight budget, there are programs and assistance that you can tap into.

Let's start with volunteers. First of all, you may have family members who are able and willing to help. We relied heavily on Charlene's parents during the first two-and-a-half years. They were challenging years—not only because of the impact Charlene's stroke had on both of us, but because we had two new people living in our home. Under the best of circumstances, it is difficult having two families share the same space. But it was needed and I really appreciated their support.

We also have three daughters who were able to help out in their own ways. You or your loved one may have adult children, siblings, or other extended family members who would be willing to come in once a week or once a month to help out. Include everyone who will be genuinely helpful. I strongly encourage you not to include those you find toxic or depleting. You're looking for help, not more problems to solve. We had some examples of dear souls who wanted to help, but they were such high-maintenance individuals themselves that their idea of helping out included a long list of things *they* needed in order to help out. Things like a television that got certain channels (that we didn't get) and meals that they could not tolerate preparing because they were vegan and could not touch the meat without getting ill. There were personality issues as well that made Charlene feel like a prisoner in her own home because she had to behave in a way that did not infringe upon *their* likes and dislikes, favorite meals, television programs, or their desire for starting foolish arguments and controversial discussions, etc.

You may be a member of a church, a community club, or support group with members who are willing to volunteer for a specific task. Charlene and I joined a support group for stroke survivors and their spouses. It was an experience that helped us tremendously. In fact, we became very close friends with a couple that we met there. Arlene and Boyd were very similar to us in that Boyd's stroke was just like Charlene's. He too was severely speech-impaired. Boyd and Charlene enjoyed "communicating" with each other in their own special way. It was as though they spoke the same language, one that no one else could understand.

Arlene and I were also very similar. We were both strong entrepreneurs who knew how to multitask our caregiving responsibilities with our work schedule. We also knew the critical importance of how to put our own needs first. When the four of us got together, we all had the opportunity to forget our troubles for an evening. These good times gave both Charlene and me companionship with like-minded friends, as well as the occasional much-needed space from each other.

We enlisted the help of our oldest daughter, Debbie, a very organized person who took charge by scheduling helpers from our church, family members, and friends. She made a big white board and put everyone's name on it who expressed an interest in helping out. What we saw on the board was that Charlene had many friends. She was so popular that my claim to fame was to be known as "Charlene's husband."

Some would bring meals; others would drive her

to doctor appointments, while still others would just sit with her while I was at work. In addition, we also scheduled speech, physical, and occupational therapy to fill the necessary gaps to make sure I did not get overwhelmed with too much responsibility.

I discovered that friends and family really do want to help, but you really have to give them the proper direction; otherwise they won't feel comfortable helping. For example, I told a friend, "Call me when you can help out." Guess what? He never called. Instead my daughter would say, "I need you to sit from 4:00 p.m. to 8:00 p.m. this Tuesday. Is that good for you? No? Then what days and times are good for you? Thursdays from noon till 4:00 p.m.? Great! Can you bring lunch too?" I learned to be direct and assertive from her.

Lastly, research the programs or services in your community that may be able to help you on a regular basis. If your income is low enough, you may qualify for assistance from the state, the county, the city, the Veterans Administration, your local senior center, hospice, or palliative care. If not, look for affordable care or negotiate a trade with those who are trained in patient care. Community senior centers also provide valuable services, such as Meals on Wheels, adult day care for seniors and dementia/Alzheimer's patients, three-dollar lunches with musical entertainment, art lessons, Wii games, Ping-Pong, special travel deals, etc.

Create Your Team

Once you've identified the needs and those who may be able to meet those needs, start making contact. If it feels painful to ask for help, *find a friend who will support you as you ask for help.* Do whatever it takes to build your team. Here are a few helpful guidelines:

- Make your requests for help small and measureable. As I mentioned, don't ask for "help" in vague terms. Instead, see if the person is able to go grocery shopping once a week or twice a month. Make the request something that seems doable. No one wants to become sucked into endless requests. So, be concise in what you are asking for.

- Ask without a sense of blaming or shaming.

- People have the right to choose whether or not they will provide care for you and your loved one. Give them the opportunity to decide for themselves, without implying that they are obligated. You might feel that your sibling "should" help out with the care of your mother, but if you convey that emotional message, your relationship will be damaged. Ask with an open hand, and you'll have a better chance of getting a cheerful helper. If they don't feel they can help, be gracious and move on. Remember, being resentful only hurts you—not the person you feel has let you down. (It's almost like drinking poison and hoping the other person dies.) So, stay emotionally clear through this process.

- Show appreciation to those who are willing to help. Gratitude goes a long way with most people. Make sure you thank your team members every time they arrive and leave. Go out of your way to express your appreciation.

To reinforce this all-important message of continuing to take care of yourself *first* without feeling guilty, I recommend that you join a caregiver support group. In addition, you should also find an appropriate support group for your care-receiver's specific disability or condition. This will ensure that they are given a safe place to vent their frustrations and validate their feelings with like-minded people.

There are thousands of groups out there just waiting to bless you and your loved one with individuals who know exactly how you both feel. If you are really unable to attend one, then try the many online groups available. (Of course, I would recommend CaregiversCaregiver.com.)

Charlene attended a support group for stroke survivors, and I attended one for caregivers. I learned at that group that I needed to take care of myself *first* in order to take care of my wife. It was funny that both groups typically complain about each other. Support groups are a benefit to those in attendance. It helps to achieve a new level of understanding and appreciation by those who were on this same difficult journey.

Let's Talk About You

Step One: Write down the type of help you need. Be specific and time limited.

Step Two: Make a calendar with the needed time slots.

Step Three: Make a list of people who have volunteered to help, or who you think would help if asked.

Step Four: Make phone calls and fill in the spaces.

CHAPTER 7

SAY "YES" TO FUN; SAY "NO" TO GUILT

CHARLENE AND I first met while on a sailing trip off the coast of Southern California. We were out living our lives–having fun and enjoying ourselves. I was knocked off my feet with her beauty. I also had the amazing pleasure of tasting her gourmet cooking. Since the way to a man's heart is through his stomach, we obviously married. We shared a similar sense of humor and a zest for life that bonded us quickly. Our beautiful home became the social center of our friendship circle. We loved to entertain, and everyone loved Charlene's dishes.

Her stroke did not change the fact that we both insisted on enjoying our lives. Of course, her physical limitations and my new role as full-time caregiver significantly altered our relationship and some of our options. Fortunately, technology has helped us become more mobile. She owns a specialized van with a mobility lift, and recently we were able to afford a four-wheel-drive wheelchair that goes up and down stairs. It also drives over all types of terrain, including the soft sand at the beach. But, as I've stated previously in this book, Charlene refuses to let the stroke stop her creativity, her communication with other people, or her enjoyment of each and every day.

We share this determination—and I think my insistence on having a fulfilled life is the cornerstone of my ability to care for her over many, many years. At the heart of this insistence is my faith in God— who I believe has a purpose for my life beyond being a caregiver. Life is bigger, and my role in it is broader than the care of my wife. I see her life in this same way. She is more than a stroke survivor—she is a wonderful wife, mother, homemaker, friend and creative daughter of God.

The loved one you care for has a larger purpose in God's eyes than simply surviving. To the extent that they can discover this purpose and invest themselves in it, they will be able to enjoy their lives in spite of their limitations. Whether or not your loved one can see their larger role in life, it's critical that you see yours. After all, *It's Your Life, Too!* God has a reason for you to be on this planet, and you will find fulfillment and joy through this endeavor. I have noticed that Charlene's new purpose in life is encouraging others who see that, while she cannot talk and cannot walk, she is so amazing that she makes us normal people look like whiners and complainers. My new purpose is to constantly be humbled by the privilege of being her caregiver and husband. Anytime I feel like complaining about my little aches and pains, I look at her and realize that she has it a hundred times worse and doesn't complain—she has a smile on her face and faith in her heart that everything is going to be OK. I think this is a very important purpose in life: to encourage one another.

Drop the Guilt

Many of the caregivers I work with do not believe they deserve to have fun. They will ask me, "How can I enjoy myself when my loved one is suffering?" or "How can I leave them and go out with other people? All I can think of is how sad or upset they are with me." Guilt is an emotion that lets us know we have broken one of God's moral laws, like the Ten Commandments. We are to respond to guilt by taking responsibility for whatever we've done that is legitimately hurtful, ask for forgiveness and make amends.

There are two types of guilt: deserved guilt and undeserved guilt. Let's start with deserved guilt. Deserved guilt is based in our conscience, which is supposed to be the police officer of our actions. Unless one suffers from certain types of mental illness, everyone has a sense of "right and wrong." We don't always agree about which actions are right or which actions are wrong, but every culture has an understanding that some behaviors are accepted and others aren't. Your conscience has been programmed by your upbringing, your parents, your church, your government, yourself, or anybody else with authority who is supposed to know the difference between right and wrong.

Although it is true that all situations are not strictly black-and-white, most would hopefully agree that the Ten Commandments are the best place to determine absolute ethics, since the Bible has withstood the test of time for over four thousand years. These ethics include: don't lie, don't steal, don't sleep with your neighbor's spouse, honor your parents, don't covet other people's stuff, treat others as you would treat yourself, don't swear or curse, love God, and don't put anything or anybody above Him. I believe that these are good values to have in your conscience for a society to successfully function.

If your conscience was formed correctly while you were growing up, it will serve as the moral judge and jury for the decisions you make. When you feel guilty, the first thing you need to do is ask yourself, "Is there a legitimate reason that I should feel this guilt?" If the answer is "Yes," then correct the wrong. Apologize to the person, fix what you broke, call who you should have called, and turn yourself into the police. Whatever it is, fix it! Then take the guilt and dispose of it, never to be seen or felt again. Guilt will periodically come to every conscience; it's just a fact of life when you live with other human beings in this world. Just deal with it properly and immediately.

Think about the last time that you were offended by somebody. Did you apologize? If so, how did you ask for forgiveness? Did you simply say, "I'm sorry," and walk away? Did you cry? Did you look them in the eye to let them see your regret, shame and sorrow? Did you promise never to do it again? Was your offense a repeated wrongdoing that made them not accept your apology or distrust your constant promises to never repeat the transgression?

Have you ever had someone say they were sorry,

but you didn't feel that they were really sorry? Did you think they said they were sorry only because they got caught? Did you feel like they would continue to commit the offense against you or others? It's very difficult these days to find responsible adults who know how to sincerely apologize and can actually feel remorse for their offenses.

The actual word "repent" in the Greek language literally means to change your mind (which will change your behavior). In other words, one must do a 180-degree turn around and go in the opposite direction. A more modern definition from the *Merriam-Webster Dictionary* says, "To feel or show that you are sorry for something bad or wrong that you did and that you want to do what is right."

Unless you are genuinely sorrowful and repentant, your apology won't be taken seriously. If the offense is related to some sort of addiction or compulsion, then get the appropriate help that you need to insure that the wrongdoing does not occur again.

But, in some instances, we cannot trust our consciences because of an abusive upbringing or an authority figure who has distorted the programming of what we have been taught is genuinely right or wrong. Incest is an example of such a distortion. Today especially, the fine line between right and wrong has been blurred because of society's decision to move from believing in absolute ethics to situational ethics—different shades of gray instead of black-and-white depending on the situation. I'm writing about ethics because guilt is a reason why ethics gets fuzzy.

While I want my conscience to let me know if I violate moral truths, I felt guilty for things that were beyond my control. I felt guilty about not anticipating Charlene's stroke and not being more informed to prevent it from happening. I'd tell myself, "If only I had known more about strokes and how it can negatively change a life forever, my wife might still be walking and talking today."

Charlene had none of the risk factors for stroke. She was healthy, her blood pressure was normal, and she had no family history of heart disease, stroke, or high cholesterol. She was neither a heavy drinker or a smoker. The doctors never pinpointed a reason for the blood clot that blocked the carotid artery in her neck and caused her stroke. It could have even been the progesterone/estrogen pills that she was on at the time. It is now reported that hormone therapy, as well as birth control pills (which she was *not* on) can cause blood clots. In any event, her three day "headache of my life" was the only warning sign she received, but we didn't take it seriously enough. We just figured the headache would eventually go away, and that if we did go the doctor, he probably would have told us that proverbial, "Just take two aspirin and call me in the morning."

I didn't comprehend that I had the right, or even the obligation, to question the doctors about what they were doing and why. If only I had asked more questions, perhaps I would have discovered that there is only a three-hour window available to administer the clot-busting drug, tPa, to prevent a person's brain from being permanently damaged. I have told myself, "I should have done more. I could have said more. She would be normal if it wasn't for me. It's my fault that she is forever disabled."

These condemning voices filled my thoughts. Playing the "should'a, could'a, would'a" game is never productive. Hindsight is always 20/20 vision. There was no way that I could have *ever* known everything that I needed to know back then (or even into the future for that matter).

When struggling with guilt, my emotions swung back and forth. First, I'd think about how this tragedy has disrupted my plans and my life. Then I'd think about Charlene. What about her? She is the one whose body is affected by a debilitating stroke. She is the one who is paralyzed on her right side and can no longer speak in sentences. What am I complaining about? How selfish of me!

Then I felt guilt for thinking such thoughts. I was so confused. What was happening to me? Why were we going through this trial? Was there sin in our lives that we were being judged for? Now I had a huge headache. I prayed, "Lord, make it stop. Please, make it stop. Let me wake up from this and let it all be a bad dream."

The next question to ask yourself is, "Is the guilt that I feel *undeserved*?" If the answer to this question is yes, then there is no wrong to correct, no apology is necessary, nothing to fix, nothing broken, no one to call or no jail to be sentenced to. You are innocent; the guilt is not based in fact. However, make sure that you can be honest, fair, and objective about your answer. If you are not sure, then ask the opinion of a well-respected mentor. If the answer is still that it's undeserved guilt, then take that guilt and dispose of it. You never have to see it or feel it again.

Whether you are genuinely guilty of hurting someone, or you're suffering from underserved guilt feelings, take care of the situation. Apologize and make amends if needed, or let go of the false guilt. In either case, the guilt is gone, and your conscience is clear. This requires an honest look at yourself and your behavior. Remember, taking care of yourself, while making sure your loved one has quality (not perfect) care, is nothing to feel guilty about.

Your guilt meter may be broken. Just because you feel guilty doesn't make you guilty. It may take a conscious decision to simply say, "No" when you or any other person blames you for putting your needs above your care-receiver (that is called self-care). Your life is just as important as it was before your loved one's illness or accident. Living your life to the fullest is not a bad thing—it is fulfilling God's plan for your life. Whether no one else supports you, or even if your loved one is upset with you, it's critical for your survival to create opportunities for you to have fun, to replenish your energy, and to dream beyond your caretaking role. *It's Your Life, Too!*

Have Some Fun

You can enjoy life with your loved one, and without.

- Have fun together: Charlene and I have fun together. As I mentioned before, we are fortunate enough to have a handicap van with a lift which friends can use to take her on outings, dinner, or a movie. We have a date night each week. On Sundays, we go to church and out for lunch afterwards.

- Attend a support group: It is important for a caregiver to find and attend a support group so that you have a safe place to vent, share experiences, and come up with solutions to problem situations. It was at my first caregiver support group that I learned that I needed to take care of myself *first* in order to take care of my wife.

- Have fun apart: I usually take one full day a week off from caregiving duties. You may need less, or you may need more. I plan ahead and make sure Charlene has someone to care for her. And I take the entire day to do whatever I want. I may read or go sailing or visit a friend. My activities change from week to week according to my needs. That one day is for my benefit, (and Charlene's as well).

In addition, twice a year, I take her to her mom's or her aunt's house in Central California for a week, and we both have some time away from each other. Charlene loves being with her favorite aunt, and she loves to spend time with her mom. I love having a break from the normal day-to-day caregiving routine. It is healthy for both of us. It takes some planning, but we both look forward to these fun times. A win/win!

It is a special treat for me to get away from my reality and share my feelings with safe people who are not a part of my situation back home. I'm sure you can think of other ways to put your needs first—maybe by getting a massage, going to a ball game with a friend, catching a movie, going fishing, or even just going to Starbucks to have a conversation with a pal.

I'll admit that sometimes I feel guilty—like I'm cutting school. I find myself thinking about Charlene and wondering if she's upset with me, or question whether or not I deserve the day off. But I've learned over the years to acknowledge this false sense of guilt and turn my attention back to *my* needs. It takes practice to ignore false guilt, because it comes at us from all directions. I have learned to ignore that feeling because I *know* I need that respite, and I don't even debate it in my mind anymore.

I no longer consider the days that I put myself first as being selfish, because that is how I managed to survive all these years since 1996 as my wife's caregiver, and with a smile on my face. This is why I don't burn out any more. I've learned that charging your cell phone when it reaches 20 percent instead of waiting for it to flash 1 percent and then quit on you when you need it the most is the better solution.

Setting this up isn't easy—at least it wasn't for me. The key is to plan in advance, and ask someone for help, so you can arrange much needed breaks. As I mentioned before, you can find somebody who may not provide as good a care to your loved one as you would, but that is OK. As long as it is adequate care, don't feel guilty when your care-receiver complains that the substitute caregiver didn't serve the coffee hot enough, or they were talking on the phone too much.

Explain to them (and know for yourself) that your care is probably the best care they will ever receive from anyone; however, unless you can take breaks and depend on this substitute person's "adequate" care, then your loved one could be receiving no care at all because you will probably burnout. Don't allow your care-receiver to be so demanding of you that you sacrifice your health for theirs. Both lives are equally important.

Let's Talk About You

Enjoy life in spite of your circumstances. Create a fun atmosphere.

1. Carve out a little time in your schedule for your own hobbies and interests.
2. Keep a network of friends and caregiver support groups–don't isolate yourself.
3. Always maintain a hopeful and positive attitude.
4. Get organized.

CHAPTER 8

SAY "YES" TO GRATITUDE;
SAY "NO" TO RESENTMENT

IT MAY SEEM ridiculous to talk about gratitude when you're going through something as difficult as you are facing right now. Who in their right mind would be grateful for tragedy and loss? I used to resent people who responded with platitudes and well wishes without the slightest idea of what Charlene and I were facing, day in and day out.

I admit that I am not grateful for Charlene's stroke. If I could change what occurred, I would. I don't think it is biblically sound or psychologically healthy to pressure anyone to conjure up gratitude for a tragedy.

However, we have a choice, no matter what challenges come to us in life, to live with an attitude of gratitude. There are a great many things for which I am thankful. And, without nurturing a sense of gratitude, we long-term caregivers often fall into deep resentment—a toxic and life-draining mind-set that leads nowhere but to burnout.

Faith in God's Purpose in My Life

It would be impossible for me to come to the realizations that I have over the past many years without a faith in God. I meet a lot of caregivers, and almost all of them have resigned themselves to the fact that, if there is a God, He has "allowed" or "willed" their particular situation to happen for whatever reason to their loved one (and to them as well). I don't want to get into a theological debate here, as that is not my area of expertise. But I think that the way we see God and our purpose in life is foundational for us to avoid burnout and live lives of gratitude.

I believe that we live in a sinful world that is full of disease, disasters and danger. Sounds a bit dramatic, but let's be honest here. No one has been promised that they will not suffer in this life—not the most faithful believer in the world can escape the realities of this world. At the same time, I don't believe that God wants us to suffer. To the contrary, the Bible repeatedly teaches us how to live holy, righteous lives and to take care of each other. If everyone followed the Ten Commandments alone, imagine how different our world would be.

The promise of God is simple: No matter what happens to us, God is with us and will bring surprising and life-changing good out of the situation. That's an amazing promise! We go through nothing all alone, and good will always result from whatever comes our way. For that promise, I am deeply grateful.

With this understanding, it makes sense when I read 1 Thessalonians 5:16 (NLT). It says, "Give thanks in all circumstances; for this is God's will for you in Christ Jesus." We're not being asked to be thankful *for* all of our circumstances, but to be thankful *in* our circumstances. There's quite a difference in these two perspectives.

Thankfulness is a wonderful thing. It takes your mind off your problems (the things you've lost), and it focuses on the blessings you still have. There is a famous saying about a man who was complaining that he had no shoes—that is, until he met a man with no feet. Then that man was also complaining because he had no feet, until he met a man with no legs, and so the story goes.

People often come up to me and tell me how sorry they are for me having a wife who has not been able to speak or walk since 1996. They ask me how I do it, and say they could never do what I am doing. I explain to them that it is God's grace that He has freely given to me, that I cannot take any credit for it. I don't have the grace to go through having an autistic child, but that parent doesn't have my grace to go through having a wife who suffered a stroke. God's grace is tailor-made for each person.

The good news is that He has designed our particular trials to perfect us and teach us perseverance and to develop character in us. 1 Peter 1:7 (NLT) says, "These trials are only to test your faith, to show that it is strong and pure. It is being tested as fire tests and purifies gold—and your faith is far more precious to God than mere gold. If your faith remains strong after being tried by fiery trials, it will bring you much praise and glory and honor on the day when Jesus Christ is revealed to the whole world."

Let me share with you the analogy of an actor performing on a stage to help make my point. When the curtain goes up on the stage, the actor steps out into the spotlight and says his lines that he has rehearsed for weeks, or maybe even months. Life is like that stage. When we go through our trials in life, it's like we are rehearsing our lines for our part in a play. We may have to rehearse our lines for weeks, months, or maybe even years. Like those lines in the play that we rehearse, our trials similarly are the rehearsals for our destiny, and our performance in the production called life.

God (the producer) assigns us our perfect part in the play, according to our personality, training, temperament, and experience. He then casts that part exclusively for us. No one else is capable or qualified to play our part in this play. So, when that curtain goes up, and it's time to perform, we must rise to the occasion and do what we have been preparing to do with excellence. For example, someone who has experienced a life of child molestation might decide to finally deal with all the hurt and pain as they reach adulthood.

This allows God to minister healing through counseling and therapy, which brings the healed person to a place where forgiveness is offered, not only for his abuser, but also for himself. After being healed of his shattered life, he is now able to help others find their way to receive the same healing and forgiveness that released them from the paralyzing hold that it once had on their life.

God always has a purpose for the trials that we experience in life that cause us so much pain. I wouldn't be writing this book, and hopefully helping others who are also struggling to overcome life's unbelievable hardships, if I hadn't personally gone through hardships myself. If Charlene and I can survive our trials with a joyful peace, then so can you. Like I said, God always has a purpose in your trials. Just submit to his will, and don't give up or lose faith. "Do not become weary in doing good, for at the proper time you will reap a harvest if you do not give up." (Galatians 6:9).

An Attitude of Gratitude

It has been said that genius is 1 percent inspiration, and 99 percent perspiration. Humans were made to be goal oriented. "Where there is no vision, the people perish" (Proverbs 29:18, KJV). Boredom will usually creep in if we are not striving towards a goal. Balance, however, is the necessary ingredient in any genius; otherwise the line that separates genius and insanity gets blurry. We get into trouble whenever we get out of balance. Too much work, too much play, too much anything makes us unbalanced.

Get into the habit of turning your lemons into lemonade, which reminds me of a very old story that I will retell only for the benefit of those who may never have heard it. There once was a very optimistic boy who had an extremely positive attitude about life. He was told to go shovel out the horse manure from the barn. Well, he tore into that manure with a shovel like a madman. When asked why he was shoveling so enthusiastically, he replied, "Well, with all of this horse manure, there just has to be a pony in here somewhere." Now that's a positive attitude.

I've even learned lessons from the movie *Finding Nemo*. Dora and Marlin were trapped in the whale, and they were hanging onto it's uvula for their lives. Then Dora heard a voice that said, "Just let go and everything will be fine." Well, the situation was hopeless, and they had nothing to lose, so they both reluctantly let go, wondering if they were falling to their death. Instead, they fell into a pool of water, and were then blown out of the whale via its blow hole.

The moral of this story is to always have hope, never give up, and to listen to the still small voice in our heads. I know... not very scientific... but it worked for them, and it always seems to work for Charlene and me.

I have a poster on my wall with a quote from Pastor Chuck Swindoll. It reads:

> The more I live, the more I realize the impact of attitude on life. Attitude to me is more important than facts. It is more important than the past, than education, than money, than circumstances, than failures, than successes, than what other people think or say or do. It is

more important than appearance, giftedness or skill. It will make or break a company . . . a church . . . a home. The remarkable thing is we have a choice every day regarding the attitude we will embrace for that day. We cannot change our past . . . we cannot change the fact that people will act in a certain way. We cannot change the inevitable. The only thing we can do is play on the one string we have, and that is our attitude. I am convinced that life is 10% what happens to me and 90% how I react to it.

Life should be fun, and you have the power to make it fun. See the glass as half-full, and not half-empty. In this anxiety-ridden, modern, fast-paced world, 95 percent of what we worry about never comes to pass. Happiness is very contagious, but so is worry. Choose to be happy, regardless of your circumstances. Again, if Charlene and I can do it, I know *you* can.

Remember, it is not only the patient who has suffered loss; the caregiver has also. It might be the lost health of the loved one, the loss of freedom as a result of the caregiving duties, the loss of a close relationship that has changed, retiring from a work career or activity that has helped shape who they are, or anything else that has affected the caregiver's normal routine. Unawareness (or worse, denial) of their own grief process can prevent the caregiver from realizing that he or she is at risk of grief or burnout. The natural tendency is to feel invincible, to come to their loved one's rescue, not realizing the physical, emotional, and financial enormity of the situation at hand. Getting the essential Information is the key; ignorance can be deadly.

Accept God's Grace

I believe that God gives us additional wisdom, endurance, and patience—well beyond what we are capable of as mere human beings. This assistance is always available to us, but if we don't recognize and accept it, we lose out.

I am grateful that God is with me every day, giving me what I, and no other human being, can give. Why am I not lonely? Why am I content with not walking on the beach with my wife, or having those deep, intimate conversations? I believe that God has blessed me with a thing called grace. I like to call it "Charlene grace"—spiritual support that comes only from God so that I can fulfill my commitment to Charlene.

Thankfully, Charlene is also gifted with something

called "David grace." I believe Charlene grace and David grace is something that God has put into our temperaments and personalities to make us align with each other. Most of the time, what would normally irritate us about one another is replaced by peace and contentment.

Grace is a good thing. I am also appreciative that God has put an attraction in our hearts toward each other. My wife takes a lot of baloney from me. Thank God she has the grace to deal with me. Grace is a gift that is available to anyone who recognizes it. Charlene is also very happy now, even when I am being very difficult. God has given her favor towards me. Acknowledging His presence is the first step in achieving peace and freedom, in my opinion. I believe that it is an essential ingredient for caregivers to survive their ministry.

There is always a way out of your impossible predicament. The Bible says, "All things are possible to those who believe" (Mark 9:23). So many people quit too early, not realizing they were so close to their breakthrough.

I heard a story about a man who was rappelling a mountain and lost his footing, falling several hundred feet, but a tree caught his body and broke his fall. He was left hanging on a branch by his rope. There was a very dense fog, and he couldn't see how far the ground was below him. That night the temperature was below freezing, and when they found him the next morning, he had frozen to death –hanging just five feet off the ground (that he could not see because of the fog). He was also only a quarter mile from a campsite.

He must have given up all hope, instead of taking a risk, and simply cutting his rope to fall the five feet to his survival. Now it is true that he did not know the ground was only five feet below him, but he had absolutely nothing to lose, and only his life to gain, if he had just realized that he was going to freeze to death anyway if he did nothing. He at least would have had a fifty/fifty chance of surviving the fall, and finding shelter for the night. Instead he chose to do nothing and died by simply giving up.

Trials Grow Character in Us
(Whether We Like It or Not!)

How did Charlene and I make it through all of these trials? One day at a time, and one miracle at a time, having faith every single day. Oh sure, there were some days that we may have struggled with our faith and momentarily forgot about God's promises, but then we would feel the anxiousness of fear begin to creep into our spirits and start to rob us of our joy and peace.

That would remind us to run, not walk, back to His promises and His presence. My positive attitude toward life, along with Charlene's positive attitude toward her recovery, has certainly been a process. I can assure you it did not happen overnight. It starts with a core belief that all things happen for a reason. We don't always have to know what that reason is. Charlene and I believe there is a Creator—a Higher Power—who controls all things, and at times allows bad things to happen to good people.

As I mentioned earlier in this chapter, we have spoken to many stroke survivors over the years, and it is very difficult to find any who do not have faith in God or trust Him in their daily circumstances. The human spirit is a marvelous thing to behold. I often think of people who have faced tremendous odds. These individuals could not have survived if it weren't for their faith. This faith is the force that keeps them going in the face of otherwise insurmountable odds.

I often wonder why some people are chosen to endure greater hardships in life than others. After many years of life experience and much contemplation, I have come to the following conclusion: God gives greater trials to certain individuals in order to bring out their unusual positive character traits that they might not otherwise have known they possess.

In fact, if it wasn't for the great hardships that God allows in their lives, they would not achieve the level of greatness and strength of character they were born to attain. There are numerous people who have survived and conquered their trials, such as Helen Keller, who rose to greatness because of her disability. She paved the way for others who were blind and wanted to live more normal lives. The list of famous people with disabilities is staggering. Google it sometime, and prepare to be shocked by the endless list of individuals who achieved greatness despite their particular ordeals. For example, some famous on the autism spectrum include, Albert Einstein, actress Daryl Hannah, and Peter Tork of The Monkees. Howard Hughes, Dan Ackroyd, and Wolfgang Amadeus Mozart all were believed to have Tourette's Syndrome. The list seems endless.

How do these amazing people against seemingly insurmountable odds defy logic as they overcome their challenges each day? The common thread among them seems to be faith. I mentioned this verse earlier in this chapter, but it bears repeating again: The Bible reminds us that, "These trials will show that your faith is genuine. It is being tested as fire tests and purifies gold—though your faith is far more precious to God than mere gold" (1 Peter 1:7, NLT).

I have seen amazing occurrences time and time again with my wife. She overcame her struggles in life, and so can you. For example, she cannot speak more than a handful of words, nor can she speak in full sentences. Yet she can have a fifteen-minute "conversation" with a total stranger who has just met her for the first time. They are captivated by her outward and inward beauty without realizing that she is speech-impaired while she "communicates" with them.

How does she do this? I witnessed her "speaking" to an elderly gentleman who was waiting for a table at a busy restaurant. He saw Charlene and asked her how she was doing. She looked him right in the eyes and with a great big Charlene smile, she shook her head up and down and said, "Ahhhhhhh." Then she tilted her head back and closed her eyes with that big smile still on her face. She brought her head forward, looked him right in the eyes again with that same big smile. She lifted her eyebrows and extended a hand with palm facing upward to him as if to say, "And you?"

He knew instinctively that she was asking him how he was. He shared his own experiences that day with this attractive woman who seemed very interested in what he had to say. She responded with a host of gestures and sounds—a nod, a laugh, a raising of her eyebrows, a wrinkling of her nose, a wink, or by making some other appropriate sounds.

She uses her tonality to say the same word differently. She may also make hand gestures or point. As people feel more comfortable talking to her, she might also touch their face, hand, or leg. It is said that 85 percent of communication is non-verbal, and Charlene uses every ounce of non-verbal communication to make up for her lack of vocabulary. The point is that Charlene has taken inventory of all the gifts that she still has, and she uses every one of the resources that are still at her disposal. Yes, much was taken away from her, but even more was left in her possession. It is her attitude (and yours) that makes all the difference in the world. If *anyone* has a right to feel sorry for themselves, Charlene does. But she never "goes there," and you shouldn't either. It is unproductive and only causes harm.

Likewise, you can also remind *yourself* of what you still have, instead of what you have lost. This is not to minimize your loss, but to hopefully move you out of your self-pity and into a new mindset and attitude. You will then be able to see yourself more equipped to do a new thing, a new ministry, a new work, and to possess a new life. That is much better than just rolling over and giving up, isn't it?

We are all so fortunate to be living in an age where our government has insured the rights and accessibility of the disabled with the passage of the Americans with Disabilities Act of 1990. Using my wife again to further illustrate my point, let's look at her paralysis problem. She can't walk and is immobile, but thanks to technology, that is no longer a problem. As I mentioned before, Charlene owns a folding electric wheelchair that makes her very mobile, especially in her van equipped with a wheelchair lift. She's able to travel almost anywhere around the world. Her electric wheelchair will take her on the road, on a plane or on a cruise ship. She has many hobbies, such as cooking and preparing elaborate gourmet dinner parties and table settings.

Her other hobbies include home decorating, sewing, furnishing her miniature doll house, and making doll clothes—despite having the use of only one arm that works. Check out our website where you can view a video about her life. It includes links for caregiver resources, our radio show podcasts, YouTube videos, our blog, and a place to order books. Please visit www.CaregiversCaregiver.com for more information.

Why am I again constantly talking about my amazing wife? Because, as a caregiver, if my care-receiver can be happier, have more purpose in life, or just feel better about her disability, then my life as a caregiver will also benefit from those great positive changes. One of the duties listed on my and your caregiver job description is to encourage and challenge your loved one to be all that they can be after their disability occurred. This includes: Alzheimer's, cancer, stroke, spinal cord injury, broken bones, blindness, brain injuries, deaf/hard of hearing, learning disabilities, physical disabilities, psychological disabilities, speech and language disabilities, hyperactivity disorders, autism, etc.

Charlene is an amazing example of a great care-receiver (who also frustrates me sometimes). I hold my loved one in very high regard, but as I've mentioned, sometimes when I try to encourage her or challenge her to do her best at overcoming a particular obstacle, it seems like she doesn't appreciate my efforts. She feels that she can do it on her own terms and in her own time. As frustrating as that is for me, I am tempted to just cross that one off my job description list, but I don't, and you shouldn't either. They *may* be listening to you, and you just might have planted a seed that may take a few days or weeks to germinate. Just be patient and continue to do and say what is right, no matter what reaction you may get.

I Am Grateful for My Ministry to Caregivers

Something I never expected (or even wanted) was a ministry to help others like myself who are long-term caregivers. But that has been one of the most enjoyable and inspiring opportunities to come from our personal tragedy. Thousands of caregivers listen to my radio shows where I interview the leading experts in burnout prevention, caregiving issues and support building. I invite you to go to my website and take advantage of the amazing information and contacts available to you.

At the beginning of this book I stated that you might feel alone, but you're not alone. I'm here for you, along with your personal support network and other caregivers who are willing to encourage you. Again, please go to my site at www.CaregiversCaregiver. com as well as like my Facebook page, "Dave, The Caregiver's Caregiver," and sign up today to become part of the tens of thousands of caregivers who have already joined our ever-expanding community. We have a free gift waiting for you. Check it out.

Let's Talk About You

Take some time to identify the many positive things that have come into your life. Tell God how grateful you are for the many blessings that He has bestowed upon you. Know that you are being given the grace you need for your specific challenge.

Remember, your life is as important as anyone else's, and that includes your loved one. Your attitude of gratitude will help prevent resentment and burnout so that you can enjoy the life you deserve and fulfill your life's purpose.

Special thanks to the Spinal Cord Injury (SCI) support group for this useful exercise. This is one of my favorite tools to work through any misunderstandings that help you feel heard without anyone feeling attacked.

The Love Letter

Level 1: Anger
I don't like.......................
I resent..........................
I feel frustrated..................
I feel angry......................
I feel furious....................
I want............................

151

Level 2: Sadness
It hurts...............................
I feel disappointed..............
I feel sad............................
I feel unhappy.....................
I wish................................

Level 3: Fear
It is painful.........................
I feel worried.....................
I feel afraid........................
I feel scared.......................
I need..............................

Level 4: Remorse and Apologies
I apologize.........................
I feel embarrassed...............
I am sorry..........................
I feel ashamed....................
I am willing........................

Level 5: Love, Understanding, Gratitude, and Forgiveness
I love...............................
I appreciate........................
I realize.............................
I forgive............................

Thank you........................
I would like........................
I trust.............................

Love, _____

Remember, when it is hard to be loving, it is time to write a love letter. After writing the love letter, take the time to write a response letter. In this way, you are indirectly giving yourself the love you deserve.

THE NEXT STEP

I LOVE AND appreciate you all. As caregivers, sometimes it seems like we are in the same leaky boat together, and we must either pick up a bucket to start bailing or sink. Perhaps buying this book was your very first step in actually caring for yourself. I sincerely hope that this book has started you on that all-important journey of *self-care*. Now let's continue to support each other in this essential mission. May I now be so bold as to share with you what I believe could be your next step.

When I think back to when I first became a caregiver, and the two-and-a-half hard years that followed, I could have really benefitted from the ongoing support and resources that I am now offering in my amazing caregiver support package. Let's face it, a caregiver's work is never done, and new challenges come up every day. Unlike other support groups that only meet every week or so and may not address your immediate needs, our caregiver community is available 24/7 and has resources on every topic imaginable—not to mention the option for personalized coaching.

If you are really serious about wanting to stay healthy and survive this caregiving thing, then let me help you put in place the tools that you are going to need to make it through your journey—not just surviving, but thriving! Every day I meet caregivers who want things to get better, and they complain about how hard it is. Well, it is hard, very hard. I have learned that when we are in a complaining mode, we see things from a very negative and fatalistic perspective. Comments like, "I can't get anyone to help me, I have no money, I wish I could find some time to take a break," all seem very true from a negative, complaining perspective.

Please don't get mad at me, but without minimizing your situation, it is a fact that with a more positive, problem-solving attitude, we begin to find solutions to the many different problems that are common to caregiving that were not obvious to us before. Perhaps we may get inspired to cleverly come up with a new way to solicit help from people (friends or strangers) that never occurred to us before. Maybe we will find a way to start a new business from our garage or the Internet by investing an hour a day while our loved one is sleeping. Any successful entrepreneur will tell you that to be successful in anything, even caregiving, it's all about attitude and the people we surround ourselves with. We all know that actions speak louder than words, so imagine how things could change for you if you purposely surrounded yourself with amazing problem-solving caregivers who have been where you have been. Think of the wealth of knowledge and wisdom from that group alone that you can glean from. This is the true value of our group, a win/win for everyone.

Without daily support and accountability, caregivers just can't survive. They will be caught in a self-destructive death spiral. However, through the faith, hope, and love that I and our caregiver community provide, you can thrive and triumph over the urge to give up, like I almost did.

Just think of it, a place, by invitation only, where you can feel safe and comfortable, sharing your most intimate feelings and frustrations with others who empathize with you, encourage you, and remind you to take one day at a time to maintain healthy habits so you don't fall into the dangerous trap of self-pity. In other words, much needed accountability, which helps you avoid isolation and burnout. Sometimes just knowing that you made an investment in our community (and yourself) and having a real "stake" in the group keeps you consistently coming back

So, with all that said, I hope you seriously consider the benefits of joining our community of loving, understanding and wise caregivers. When you realize that the value is so much greater than the cost of getting sicker than the person you are caring for, or even the cost of your cable bill, while you sit in front of the TV for hours "vegging" (just sayin'), the decision is a no-brainer. To find out more about this next step, or if you are ready to sign up now, just go to www.CaregiversCaregiver.com.

Remember, every caregiver's life is a love story. Let me help you make that love story one of *hope* and *triumph*. Let us love on you, and be your support system. God bless you, and thank you for all you do as caregivers.

Dave, The Caregiver's Caregiver

Other books that I have authored:

And books that I have co-authored:

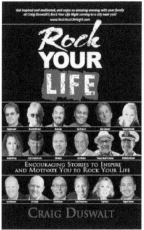